WONDERS *of* CREATION
multi-age format

THE NEW

ASTRONOMY

BOOK

DANNY R. FAULKNER

First printing: August 2014
Third printing: August 2018

Master Books
P.O. Box 726
Green Forest, AR 72638
Master Books is a division of the New Leaf Publishing Group, Inc.

ISBN: 978-0-89051-834-2
ISBN: 978-1-61458-414-8 (digital)
Library of Congress Number: 2014944220

Cover by Diana Bogardus
Interior by Terry White

Unless otherwise noted, Scripture quotations are from the New King James Version of the Bible.

Please consider requesting that a copy of this volume be purchased by your local library system.

Printed in **China**.

Please visit our website for other great titles:
www.masterbooks.com

For information regarding author interviews, please contact the publicity department at (870) 438-5288.

Master Books®
A Division of New Leaf Publishing Group
www.masterbooks.com

TABLE OF CONTENTS

WONDERS *of* CREATION

multi-age format

Dedication

To my good friend, Huey Mills,
who has faithfully dedicated
much of his life to the Christian
education of children.

Our best-selling Wonders of Creation Series is getting even better!

The series is being developed with an enhanced
educational format and integrated with a unique
color-coded, multi-skill level design to allow ease
of teaching the content to three distinct levels.

How to use this book

The New Astronomy Book has been developed with three skill levels in mind. These can be utilized for the classroom, independent study, or homeschool setting and also be customized per the abilities of the student.

> Level 1
> Level 2
> Level 3

It is recommended that every reader examine the text on the off-white background, as this is the basic skill level information related to the material. More proficient students and those with increased interest in the subject matter can then proceed to the more advanced concept levels. Additionally, the most advanced readers, after having read through all levels of the material, can use the upper-level material as a springboard for independent research and other educational assignments (research papers, oral reports, presentations, imaginative projects, etc.).

Whether using the material as a unit study, part of a curriculum, simply a book of interest, or even a reference book for other materials, *The New Astronomy Book* will engage students with amazing visuals and facilitate learning through helpful charts and diagrams where needed. As always, whether discussing futuristic missions or current understanding of the universe and its many features, God's place as Creator is honored within this informative study.

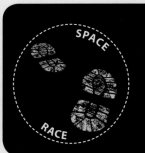

Look in the pages of the history of the race to space and the people who have influenced the world.

Level One

- Text on off-white background
- The basic level is presented for younger readers and includes the Wonder Why segments and visuals that capture student attention.

WONDER WHY?

Level Two

- Text on purple background
- This middle level delves deeper into issues related to the universe, utilizing the Mission Log (words to know) to assist with vocabulary development and comprehension.

THESE WORDS FOUND THROUGHOUT THE UPCOMING CHAPTER PRESENT A QUICK GLIMPSE OF IMPORTANT CONCEPTS COMING UP.

Level Three

- Text on blue gridded background
- This upper level incorporates more advanced concepts and theories related to all subject matter included in the text, as well as unique information that will inspire additional research or learning about advancements in space studies or man-led activities.

THE STARS OF HEAVEN

Genesis 1:1

In the beginning God created the heavens and the earth.

Introduction

> Level 1
> Level 2
> Level 3

MISSION LOG

COMET
ASTRONOMY
ASTRONOMICAL
SPECTROSCOPY
ASTROPHYSICS

What is Astronomy? Astronomy is the study of heavenly bodies, things outside of the earth. Of course, this includes the sun, moon, and stars. We know from Genesis 1:14–19 that God made the sun, moon, and stars on day 4 of the creation week. Five of the planets appear as bright stars to the naked eye, so God probably made them on day 4 as well.

In fact, any objects giving off light in the sky would have been considered stars to ancient people. An example of this would be comets. The word "comet" comes from a Latin word meaning "hairy," because ancient people thought that comets were hairy stars.

With the invention of the telescope four centuries ago, astronomers began to find many objects too faint to be seen with the eye alone. Some of these were clouds of gas and dust, while others were clusters of stars, and yet others were galaxies — huge collections of stars containing billions of stars. Biblically, we know that God made all of these on day 4.

One of the purposes for astronomical bodies that God ordained is the telling of time and using calendars (Genesis 1:14).

Indeed, the day, month, and year are defined in terms of the apparent motions of astronomical bodies. For much of history, astronomy primarily had this function, and so astronomers spent most of their time recording the movements of astronomical bodies for this purpose. Unfortunately, the God-given purposes for the astronomical bodies was soon perverted, as people began to worship the planets and stars rather than the Creator (Romans 1:25).

Men began to think that the sun, moon, and planets were gods, and so they thought that the motions of those bodies affected our lives. This developed into the religion of astrology. The religion of astrology is very different from the science of astronomy. Many people think that astrology is harmless fun, but God is not pleased with astrology or astrologers. Deuteronomy 4:19 forbids astrology, and Isaiah 47:13–14 pronounces judgment on astrologers.

THE STARS OF HEAVEN

Job 38:31

Can you bind the cluster of the Pleiade
Or loose the belt of Orion?

The invention of the telescope revolutionized astronomy, for it allowed far more detailed study than what was possible with the eyes alone. As telescopes improved, astronomers developed new instruments and new techniques, such as photography and spectroscopy. About a century ago, astronomers began to apply modern physics to the study of astronomy. They coined a new term, astrophysics, to describe this. Astrophysics has allowed us to discover far more about astronomical bodies than ever before.

The space program has played a key role in the great advancement of astronomy. Men have visited one other world, the moon. We have sent unmanned spacecraft to every planet to study them and their satellites, or moons. The earth's atmosphere hinders our view of astronomical bodies, so telescopes placed above the earth's atmosphere have greatly expanded our knowledge of astronomy.

Unfortunately, as we have increased our knowledge of the astronomical world, it seems that many people have lost sight of what is important. As Psalm 19:1 tells us, the heavens declare God's glory. That is one of the purposes of astronomical bodies. The study of astronomy ought to cause our hearts and minds to turn to Him who made the stars. The author of this book hopes that by reading this book you will dwell on the Creator and not solely upon the creature.

WONDER WHY?

What's in a word like "comet"? *The American Heritage® Dictionary of the English Language* shares this word history: "Comets have been feared throughout much of human history, and even in our own time their goings and comings receive great attention. Perhaps a comet might seem less awesome if we realized that our name for it is based on a figurative resemblance between it and humans. This figurative name is recorded first in the works of Aristotle, in which he uses *komē*, the Greek word for "hair of the head," to mean "luminous tail of a comet." Aristotle then uses the derived word *komētēs*, "wearing long hair," as a noun meaning "comet." The Greek word was adopted into Latin as *comētēs*, which was refashioned in Late Latin and given the form *comēta*, furnishing Old English with *comēta*, the earliest English ancestor of our word *comet*."[1]

The Night Sky

> Level 1
> Level 2
> Level 3

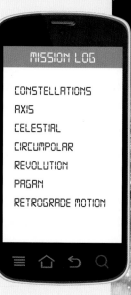

MISSION LOG

CONSTELLATIONS
AXIS
CELESTIAL
CIRCUMPOLAR
REVOLUTION
PAGAN
RETROGRADE MOTION

Probably the most obvious astronomical bodies are the stars. On a very clear, dark night, you can see thousands of stars, though the bright lights of cities may make this difficult. As you look at the sky, the stars naturally seem to group together into patterns. Ancient people saw this, and they began to give names to these patterns, and even to some individual stars. Some of the patterns faintly resemble people and animals, so ancient people named many of the patterns for various creatures. For instance, one group of stars resembles a bear, so we call it the "big bear." These patterns are called constellations.

If you watch the stars for an hour or two, you will notice that some stars rise in the east, while other stars set in the west. The sun follows the same sort of motion each day. You probably know that the earth's rotation on its axis causes the sun to move across the sky. If you guessed that the earth's rotation also causes stars to move across the night sky, you would be correct.

If you watch the motion of the stars carefully, you will notice something different from the sun's motion. Toward the north, the stars do not rise or set. Instead, they move counterclockwise in a circle around the sky. Near the center of that circle is one star, the North Star (or Polaris). The earth's rotation axis points almost directly at the North Star, so as the earth rotates, the North Star does not appear to move. Actually, the North Star does move in a small circle, because it is not exactly at the north celestial pole, the point at which the earth's rotation axis points. The North Star and stars near it are always in the sky, neither rising nor setting. These are circumpolar (meaning "around the pole") stars.

What we have just described is true only in the Northern Hemisphere. If you happen to live in the Southern Hemisphere, things will be a bit different. Circumpolar stars will be in the southern sky, and they appear to move clockwise around the south celestial pole. There is no bright star near the south celestial pole, so there is no pole star in the Southern Hemisphere.

THE STARS OF HEAVEN

Psalm 19:1

The heavens declare the glory of God; And the firmament shows His handiwork.

If you go out the next few evenings, you will notice that the stars are in about the same part of the sky at the same time on previous evenings. That is, the stars look the same from one night to the next. The stars will shift slightly to the west each night, but it takes a week or two before you may notice that. However, over a month or two, the stars will shift enough to the west that some stars that you saw previously now are no longer visible. As stars disappear in the west, other stars replace them in the east. This shift is due to our annual revolution around the sun. This causes the constellations to change from season to season. For instance, in the Northern Hemisphere, Orion is a winter constellation, but Scorpius is a summer constellation. In the Southern Hemisphere, the reverse is true.

Seeing Stars While the stars that you see each night change and the stars change each season, the stars maintain their relationships to one another, and they always return in their seasons. Many ancient pagan cultures taught that the changing stars caused the seasons to change. Job 38:31–33 mentions Orion and other constellations. This chapter in the Old Testament also discusses seasonal changes. But unlike pagan cultures, the Book of Job gives credit to God for both changing stars and seasons. Job may be the oldest book in the Bible. We don't know when Job lived, but he might have lived 4,000 years ago. Yet, when Job looked at Orion, he saw about what we see today when we look at Orion. In a sense, this gives us a direct connection to Job. More importantly, it ought to give us a direct connection to the God who made both the stars and us.

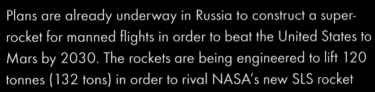

Rockets Race to the Red Planet!

Plans are already underway in Russia to construct a super-rocket for manned flights in order to beat the United States to Mars by 2030. The rockets are being engineered to lift 120 tonnes (132 tons) in order to rival NASA's new SLS rocket program (artist concept, right), which has test flights planned for 2017. There are also reports that Russia plans to establish a lunar base on the moon for long-term missions and study.[2]

SLS

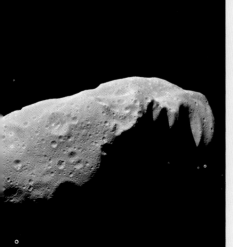

WONDER WHY?

What are NEOs? NEOs, or Near Earth Objects, are comets and asteroids that are close to our planet, and in being so close may pose a potential threat. Researchers and teams with NASA have been studying NEOs for years, trying to document their paths and potential impact to our planet. On May 3, 2014, an asteroid the size of a bus managed to get closer to Earth than even our planet's moon, having only been detected a few days before on April 28th. While many of the largest NEOs have been documented, smaller asteroids and comets are not always easily seen.[3]

We don't know who invented the constellations. Many of their names have transferred from culture to culture. We get our constellations from the ancient Greeks, who in turn got them from the ancient Egyptians. The ancient Egyptians got their constellations from the ancient Babylonians, though it isn't clear where the Babylonians got their constellations. It appears that they likely originated at about 35° latitude north around 2300 B.C. This is very close to the biblical location and date of the Tower of Babel. It makes sense that the constellations originated about that time and then spread around the world as the people dispersed after God's judgment at the Tower of Babel. Further evidence of this is that many cultures around the world have similar constellations. For instance, the big bear is common to the ancient Near East, tribes of northern Europe, and native North Americans.

We don't know what the purpose of the constellations originally was. The names and meanings probably are garbled. There is an idea that God originated the constellations, or that Adam or his son, Seth, invented them. The supposed purpose of this was to teach the gospel before there was the Bible. However, there are many problems with this theory.

While the stars remained fixed, seven bright objects don't. From night to night the moon travels eastward among the stars. It takes one month to complete one cycle around the earth. This results from the moon's orbit around the earth. In a similar manner, the sun appears to move from west to east through the stars. However, the sun's motion is much slower, taking one year to trek once around the sky with respect to the stars. Of course, this is due to the earth's revolution around the sun. (Rotation is circular motion around an axis that passes through the center of a body, while revolution is circular motion around another body.)

This is the reason why the stars that we see change from season to season. Five planets appear as bright stars in our sky. They are Mercury, Venus, Mars, Jupiter, and Saturn. Being so bright, the ancients knew these planets, and they named them. Uranus and Neptune generally are too faint to see with the naked eye, so they weren't discovered until after the invention of the telescope.

Retrograde Motion The planets normally move eastward through the stars as the sun and moon do. This is the combined motion of the earth in its orbit and the orbit of each planet. However, a planet occasionally appears to move in reverse, that is, they sometimes move east to west among the stars. Astronomers call this retrograde motion. What causes retrograde motion? In the case of superior planets, those with orbits larger than the earth's, retrograde motion happens when the earth passes the planet while the earth moves more quickly along its smaller orbit. A similar thing happens when you pass another car on the highway. While passing, the other car appears to move backward, even though it is moving forward the entire time. The inferior planets are Mercury and Venus. They have orbits smaller than the earth's. We see them retrograde when they pass us moving more quickly in their orbits. As we shall see, the ancient Greeks had some difficulty explaining retrograde motion.

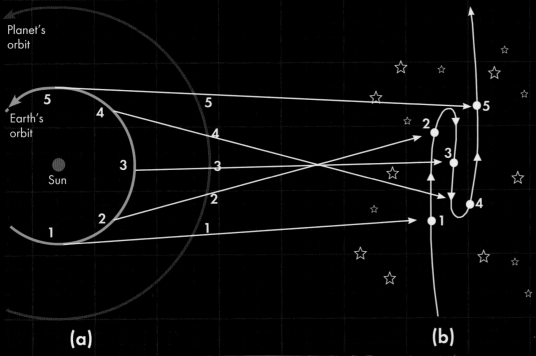

On this illustration (a), the pink line points of 1 to 5 correspond with the position of the object each time it is viewed from the five points on the blue line, representing points of viewing from Earth. Notice the difference in size of the orbit represented by the line. Notice how from points 1 to 2 the planet appears to move forward, but between points 3 and 4 it appears to move backward. By the time the planet reaches point 5, it appears to be moving forward again. The apparent backward motion between points 3 and 4 is retrograde motion.

(a)

(b)

The Moon

> Level 1
> Level 2
> Level 3

MISSION LOG

UNMANNED
LUNAR
MARIA
HIGHLANDS
ASTEROIDS
IMPACT BASINS
BOMBARDMENT

The moon is our nearest neighbor in space. It is much smaller than the earth, only being about one-fourth the earth's diameter and containing only a little more than 1 percent of the mass of the earth. Because of the earth's gravity, the moon orbits the earth. The radius of the moon's orbit is about 240,000 miles, and it takes the moon a month to orbit the earth. In fact, we get the word "month" from the moon's name.

There was much interest in manned exploration of the moon in the 1960s. In fact, that was much of the purpose of the manned space program at that time. NASA launched the Mercury and Gemini programs to develop and test our ability to live and work in space. The Mercury program had the goal of sending astronauts into space one at a time. The Gemini program sent two astronauts into space at a time and steadily increased the duration of the missions up to two weeks. Finally, the Apollo program developed and tested spacecraft to take three astronauts at a time to the moon.

The first manned lunar landing was Apollo 11 on July 20, 1969, when Neil Armstrong and Buzz Aldrin walked on the lunar surface while Michael Collins orbited the moon. Through 1972 there were five more successful manned missions to the moon. We have not been back. The Apollo landings were preceded by many unmanned missions to the moon, with one spacecraft softly landing on the lunar surface two years before Apollo 11. Only recently has NASA returned to the moon with unmanned spacecraft. There is much that we can learn about the moon and other bodies only by sending spacecraft to them.

Neil Armstrong, Michael Collins, Buzz Aldrin

THE STARS OF HEAVEN

Psalm 8:3

When I consider Your heavens, the work of Your fingers, The moon and the stars, which You have ordained.

The moon rotates on its axis at the same rate that it revolves around the earth. We call this synchronous rotation. Most of the satellites, or moons, of other planets do this, too. The result is that the moon keeps one face toward the earth at all times. We did not know what the back side of the moon looked like until after the space age, when we were able to send cameras to the other side. There is a common misconception that there is a "dark side of the moon," where the sun never shines. However, this is not true. As the moon keeps one side facing the earth as it orbits the earth, that side first is pointed away from the sun and then is pointed toward the sun. Likewise, the backside of the moon first faces the sun, and then faces away from the sun, so all parts of the moon are lit by the sun throughout each orbit around the earth.

Craters are the most familiar lunar features. Galileo was the first to see craters on the moon. What causes craters? There are two possibilities: volcanoes or impacts. Astronomers debated both theories for a long time. During the 19th century, most astronomers concluded that most lunar craters were volcanic, and this idea continued well into the 20th century. Today, we think that most lunar craters came from asteroids and comets striking the lunar surface. Craters are a common feature on many other bodies in the solar system, and we think that most of those craters came from impacts as well. However, we think that a few of the smaller craters on the moon may have come from volcanoes.

If you look at the moon, you will notice that some parts of the moon are lighter while others are darker. This is because some portions of the moon reflect light better than other portions. The lighter portions of the moon are made of rock similar to granite, while the darker areas are made of rock similar to basalt. Granite and basalt are common rocks on Earth. Granite usually is lighter than basalt. Granite is less dense than basalt, so the lighter portions of the moon are at higher elevation than the darker regions. Since the lighter regions are at higher elevation, we call them the lunar highlands. The lunar highlands appear to be rugged, because they contain many craters.

On the other hand, the darker regions are much smoother than the highlands, for they contain far fewer craters. Astronomers four centuries ago thought that the darker, smoother areas might be bodies of water, so they called them seas.

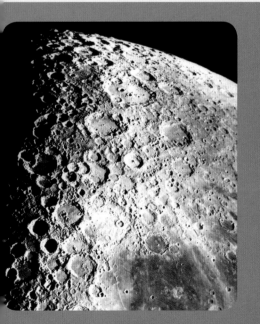

We usually use the Latin word for seas, *maria* (pronounced "mah' ree-a"). This word is plural — the singular is *mare* (pronounced "mah' ray"). Why do the maria have so few craters compared to the highlands? We think that volcanic material rose onto the lunar surface and flowed over the maria, covering most of the craters that might have been there. Most of the maria appear round, resembling very large craters. We think that sometime in the past, large bodies struck the lunar surface there, creating very large, deep craters. We call these impact basins. The impacts were so large that they cracked the lunar surface very deeply, allowing molten material to come to the surface and fill the impact basins. What about the few craters that the maria have? They must have formed from impacts after the lava had cooled.

The side of the moon that faces the earth is about evenly divided between maria and highlands. The different colors and shapes of the highlands and maria on the side of the moon that we see give the full moon the appearance of "the man in the moon." The backside the moon is very different — it is almost entirely highlands.

How do we explain the moon's features? Evolutionists think that the moon is nearly 4.6 billion years old, so they interpret its surface in terms of this great time. According to evolution, after the earth, moon, and other bodies formed, there were many pieces of leftover material left. Those objects struck the moon and all other bodies in the solar system, including the earth. Scientists call this episode of impacts the Early Heavy Bombardment (EHB), and it supposedly lasted a few hundred million years. The EHB left the entire moon heavily cratered, and many of the highland craters formed at this time. The EHB was followed by a few hundred million years of the Late Heavy Bombardment (LHB). The largest impacts occurred in the

LHB. These impacts produced the impact basins, after which lava flowed out and filled the impact basins. After the LHB, there were very few extra bodies left in the solar system, so impacts, and hence new craters, were fairly rare after that.

How might creationists interpret the moon's history? Some creationists think that craters are very bad and so could not have been part of the world until after the Fall of man, so they would place all lunar craters at the time of man's Fall or some later catastrophe, such as during the Flood. However, not all creationists agree with this. God probably did not instantly make everything during the creation week. For instance, God used a brief process to make man from dust, and He rapidly caused dry land and plants to appear on day 3. Similarly, rather than instantly forming the moon and other astronomical bodies on day 4, God may have rapidly, but miraculously, made them. If so, many lunar craters may have just been the result of the later stages of this process.

Lunar Phases

The moon does not produce its own light, but rather it merely reflects light that it receives from the sun. The sun lights half of the moon. As the moon orbits the earth, the amount of the lit half that we see changes, giving the moon a changing appearance. We call the change in the appearance of the moon *lunar phases*. We start the lunar phase cycle at new moon, when the moon is between the earth and the sun. At new moon, the moon's dark side faces the earth. At this phase, the dark half of the moon is not totally dark. We could see it, but it is up in the daytime and very close to the sun, so we cannot see it for two or three days. Eventually, the moon moves part of the way around its orbit so that we can see a thin slice of the lit half of the moon. This is the crescent phase. Over the next few evenings, the crescent grows. An old-fashioned word meaning "grow" is wax, so we call this a waxing crescent moon.

What about the maria? Recall that maria are very rare on the backside of the moon. If the large bodies that produced the impact basins fell onto the moon over many millions of years, we would expect that they would have been more evenly distributed on the moon. The fact that nearly all of them are on one side suggests that the moon was struck by a swarm of particles coming from one direction over a very brief period of time. This could have been at the time of the Flood. Perhaps impacting bodies helped start the Flood, but some of the bodies missed the earth and hit the moon on one side.

Keeping Moon Rocks Clean! According to NASA, between 1969 and 1972, six Apollo space missions brought back almost 850 pounds of moon samples — including rocks, core samples, dust, and other items. A special holding facility was created just for the samples in 1979 to keep them stored in an environment where they will not be contaminated. This means a series of steps visitors have to take just to be in proximity to the rocks. They include: putting on protective booties on shoes, removing all jewelry, putting on protective clothing, putting another set of protective booties over shoes, and even taking a one-minute "air shower" using filtered air. In this way, moon samples are preserved for further study![4]

WAXING

WANING

About a week after new moon, the moon is one-quarter of the way around its orbit, so we call this phase *first quarter*. The first quarter moon appears half lit. A few nights later, the moon is more than half lit, a phase that we call *gibbous*. Each night the lit portion of the gibbous moon grows larger, so we call this the *waxing gibbous* moon. About two weeks after new moon and about a week after first quarter, the moon appears fully lit. We call this *full moon*. The waxing phases of the moon, from new to full, are visible in the evening sky. The full moon is up all night, rising at sundown and setting at sunrise.

The lit portion of the moon shrinks after full moon, so we call the phases after full moon the waning phases (wane is the opposite of wax). Some of the waning phases may appear late at night, but all of them are visible in the early morning sky. A few days after full moon, the moon again appears gibbous, so this is the *waning gibbous* phase. The difference is that the waxing gibbous moon is lit on its right side, but the waning gibbous moon is lit on its left side. A week after full moon is *third quarter*, when the moon is half lit on its left side. Can you figure out why we call it third quarter? A few days after third quarter, the moon reaches waning gibbous. As you might anticipate, the waxing crescent is lit on the right, but the waning crescent is lit on the left. Each morning the waning gibbous moon shrinks until it disappears. This takes us back to new moon, after which the cycle repeats.

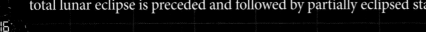

At some lunar eclipses the moon does not pass completely through the earth's planetary shadow or "umbra." When this happens, the umbra appears to take a bite out of the moon. We call this a partial lunar eclipse. The portion of the moon that is not in the earth's umbra is still bright, so it is very difficult to see what color the umbra is during a partial lunar eclipse. The portion of the moon that is not in the umbra is in the earth's penumbra, meaning partial shadow. The amount of sunlight in the penumbra is reduced from normal so the portion of the moon in the earth's penumbra isn't as bright as it usually is, but it is difficult for the human eye to tell a difference. A total lunar eclipse is preceded and followed by partially eclipsed stages.

Tides If you have spent much time near the ocean, you probably are aware of the tides. Each day, the water rises and falls about two times. Ancient people knew that the tides were delayed about 50 minutes each day, keeping time with the moon rather than the sun. The combination of our rotation and the moon's revolution around the earth causes the moon to rise on average about 50 minutes later each day. Therefore, the moon causes the tides, but how? It wasn't until Sir Isaac Newton discovered his law of gravity that this mystery was solved.

The earth's gravity pulls on the moon, causing the moon to orbit the earth. But the moon's gravity also pulls on the earth. Because the moon is so close to the earth, the moon's gravity pulls on the side of the earth facing the moon (sublunar) more than it pulls on the earth's center. And the moon's gravity pulls on the earth's center more than it pulls on the side of the earth away from the moon (antipodal). This differential force of the moon's gravity stretches the earth. This causes the earth to have a slight oblong shape with bulges pointing along a line from the earth to the moon. Notice that there is a bulge on either side of the earth, both facing the moon and away from the moon.

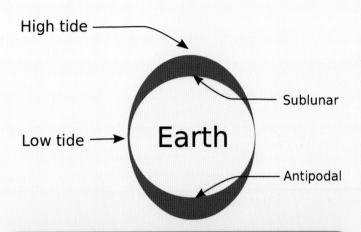

The rocks of the earth actually stretch a bit, but not enough to satisfy the total amount of stretch required. Because the oceans are relatively free to move around, they pile up on either side of the earth to make up the difference. So there is a high tide on two sides of the earth — the side facing the moon, and side away from the moon. In between are regions of low tide. The earth rotates quickly, and the tidal bulge must follow the earth's rotation, so most locations pass through nearly two high tides and two low tides per day.

The sun also produces tides, but because the sun is so much farther away than the moon, its tides aren't nearly as high. At new and full moon, both lunar and solar tides work together, and we say that this is spring tide. This name has nothing to do with the seasons. Rather, it refers to how much the tides spring, or leap, from very low levels at low tide to very high levels at high tide. On the other hand, at the quarter phases, the lunar and solar tides compete. This is neap tide. At neap tide the high tides aren't nearly as high as they are at spring tide, but the low tides aren't nearly as low as they are during spring tide. In other words, at spring tide the difference between high and low tide is large, but the difference between high and low tide is small at neap tide.

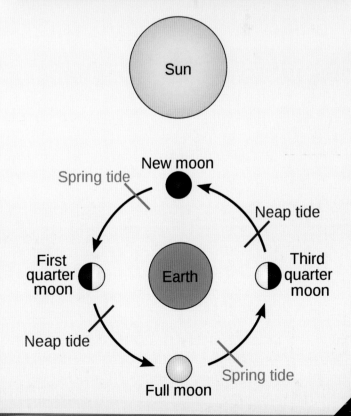

Eclipses There is a common misconception that the moon's phases are caused by the earth's shadow on the moon. However, when the earth's shadow falls on the moon, it is a lunar eclipse. The earth's shadow points away from the sun, so the only time that a lunar eclipse can happen is when the moon is full. However there is not a lunar eclipse every month when the moon is full. That is because the moon's orbit around the earth is slightly tilted to the earth's orbit around the sun. As a result, at full moon the earth's shadow usually passes above or below the moon, entirely missing the moon. A lunar eclipse happens only when the moon is near one of the two points on its orbit where it crosses the earth's orbit. Twice each year there is a period of time when this happens near a full moon so that a lunar eclipse may happen.

We call the earth's shadow the umbra, the Latin word for shadow. The earth's umbra is larger than the moon, so sometimes the umbra completely covers the moon. This is a total lunar eclipse. A totally eclipsed moon is much fainter than the full moon normally is, but it isn't completely dark. This is because the earth's atmosphere scatters and bends sunlight into its umbra. This is why the sky does not go dark immediately after sunset. The amount and color of light in the umbra varies from eclipse to eclipse. This causes each total lunar eclipse to be different. Sometimes the totally eclipsed moon is very dark, almost black. Other times it is golden, orange, or red. In 1982 there was a very unusual eclipse where part of the umbra was very dark and the other part was peach color.

At some lunar eclipses the moon does not pass completely through the earth's umbra. When this happens, the umbra appears to take a bite out of the moon. We call this a partial lunar eclipse. The portion of the moon that is not in the earth's umbra is still bright, so it is very difficult to see what color the umbra is during a partial lunar eclipse. The portion of the moon that is not in the umbra is in the earth's penumbra, meaning partial shadow. The amount of sunlight in the penumbra is reduced from normal so the portion of the moon in the earth's penumbra isn't as bright as it usually is, but it is difficult for the human eye to tell a difference. A total lunar eclipse is preceded and followed by partially eclipsed stages.

Ancient astronomers knew what caused lunar eclipses, and they noticed that the earth's umbra is always circular. They also realized that the only shape that always casts a circular shadow is a sphere. Hence, ancient astronomers knew that the earth was spherical, or round, like a ball. It is a common misconception today that people thought that the world was flat until the time of Christopher Columbus 500 years ago. The debate during Columbus's time was not over the shape of the earth. Rather, it was over the size of the earth. Columbus thought that it was smaller than most people thought, small enough that it was shorter to travel westward rather than eastward from Europe to reach Asia. As it turns out, Columbus was wrong! Why do so many people today think that belief in a flat earth was common until recently? Widespread belief in a flat earth was a myth created in the 19th century to shame Christians into accepting evolution. Critics argued that Christianity got the shape of the earth wrong, so the Church could redeem itself by embracing Darwinism. However, neither the Church nor the Bible taught that the earth was flat. In fact, some people believe that Isaiah implies that the earth is spherical (40:22).

When the moon passes between the earth and sun, the moon's shadow may fall on the earth. We call this a solar eclipse. A solar eclipse can happen only at new moon. However, there is not a solar eclipse every new moon. Like a lunar eclipse, the moon sometimes is too high or low so that its shadow misses the earth. If a new moon occurs close to the time that the moon crosses the earth's orbit, a solar eclipse may occur.

Like the earth's shadow, the moon's shadow has two parts, the umbra and penumbra. However, unlike the earth's umbra, the moon's umbra is dark, because the moon has no atmosphere. Additionally, the moon's umbra is far smaller than the earth's umbra. The moon's umbra is at most a few hundred miles across. As the moon's umbra races across the earth, people along the umbra's path see the sun darkened for a few minutes. This is a total solar eclipse.

Many strange and wonderful things happen during a total solar eclipse. Though the sky is not as dark as midnight, the brightest stars and planets may appear. Animals seek to roost. Shadow bands, faint wispy lines, move across the ground. Remember, it is never safe to look directly at the sun. Around the sun appears the pearly white corona, the outermost layer of the sun. The corona can extend a couple of diameters of the sun, and lines that trace out the sun's magnetic field are visible. Jutting out into space along the edge of the sun are blood-red prominences. Prominences are loops of gas that follow the sun's magnetic field. After a few minutes, things return to normal as totality ends. While there are many photographs of total solar eclipses, none of them truly do justice to what it is really like.

On either side of the path of totality, there are large regions on Earth within the moon's penumbra. These places experience a partial solar eclipse, where only a portion of the sun is covered. It looks like the moon has taken a circular bite out of the sun. It is not safe to look directly at a partial solar eclipse. There are safe ways to view a partial solar eclipse, such as with a pinhole camera (see diagram on right). The sky does not get dark, nor can you experience the wonderful things that happen only during a total solar eclipse. Where a total eclipse is visible, totality is preceded and followed by partial stages.

While the sun is 400 times larger than the moon, the sun is 400 times farther away. Therefore, in our sky, the sun and moon appear to be about the same size.

During a total solar eclipse, the moon just barely covers the sun. This makes total solar eclipses possible, but also rare and spectacular. If the moon were slightly smaller or slightly farther away, there would be no total solar eclipses.

The moon's orbit is an ellipse rather than a circle. If a solar eclipse happens when the moon is near apogee, the point on its orbit when it is most distant from the earth, its umbra doesn't quite reach the earth. A person near the centerline of this kind of eclipse will see a ring of the sun's surface around the moon. This is an annular eclipse. Notice that this is not annual. Rather, the term annular comes from the word annulus, meaning "ring," because there is a ring around the sun. An annular eclipse is interesting, but, like a partial solar eclipse, it is not safe to look directly at it.

Time Reckoning The day 4 account in Genesis 1 gives several purposes for the sun, moon, and stars. One of these is to mark the passage of time, to be for seasons, days, and years. We use the backdrop of the stars to mark the passage of time by watching the motion of the sun and moon. The day, the rotation period of the earth, is the most obvious natural division of time. Our bodies are designed to operate on a daily cycle in tune with the rising and setting of the sun. It is difficult for people to adjust to changing cycles, such as different patterns of work. For instance, while most people work during the day, some people work at night. For a person not used to working at night, the change to a night shift can be very disruptive. Even worse, some people work a swing shift, where their work schedule changes from day to night and back to day.

The year, the revolution period of the earth, is another obvious and natural division of time. Plants have annual growing cycles timed to changes in temperature and sunlight. Animals often reproduce and/or migrate on a similar annual cycle. Throughout history, most people were involved in farming, so this annual cycle was very important for them, too. Today, most people aren't farmers, but the annual cycle is so deeply ingrained in our thinking that we continue to observe it, such as schedules with school and vacation.

Since there are so many days in a year, it is useful to have another measurement of time intermediate between the day and year. The month works well for this. While not as important as the daily and annual cycle, there are some cycles that follow the month. For instance, ocean tides increase and decrease throughout the month. Some animals and plants have some rhythms with lunar phases. Many people think that human activity is affected by lunar phases as well. For instance, many people think that more babies are born close to full moon or that crime increases during full moon. However, studies of birth and crime statistics for large cities over many years show no evidence of this.

Amid these natural units of time we have the week. Many cultures from around the world observe the week, even though there is no natural astronomical reason to do this. Some people think that we observe the week because it is roughly one-quarter of a month. However, why would that be more important than half or one-third of the month? There really is no natural explanation for the week. The Bible reveals that God established the week when He created the world. Then at Sinai, God instructed the Hebrews that they must observe the week with the final day of the week being the Sabbath, the day of rest to commemorate the creation. The fact that the week is so universally observed is evidence of the creation.

We also need time measurements that are shorter than a day. Many cultures divided the day and the night into hours, with 12 hours in either, for a total of 24 hours in a day. Why did ancient people pick 12 rather than 10? They probably picked 12 because you can form more fractions with 12 than with 10 — ⅓ and ¼, for instance. Eventually, people divided each hour into 60 minutes and each minute into 60 seconds. Again, base 60 is divisible by more numbers than base 10. The first clocks were sundials that used the changing position of the sun's shadow as the basis of measuring time. The hands on our clocks move in the direction that the shadow on a sundial in the Northern Hemisphere moves.

Why Don't We Use a Lunar Calendar? The month is about 29½ days, and the year is nearly 365¼ days. As you can see, the day does not divide evenly into the month or year, nor does the month evenly divide into the year. There are many different ways to accommodate this. Most ancient cultures, including the Hebrews, followed a strictly lunar month. The first day of the month started when they could see the first thin waxing crescent moon after new moon. Fourteen days later, the 15th of the month, always was when the moon was full. The months usually alternated between 29 and 30 days. Twelve months was approximately 355 days, about ten days short of a full year. Thus, they added an extra month approximately every third year. The year normally began near the vernal equinox, now in our month of March. Depending upon the culture, the catch-up month was either February or March.

More than two thousand years ago, Julius Caesar scrapped the strictly lunar calendar. He did this by adding an extra ten days throughout the year. This is why most of our months are 30 and 31 days long, not 29 or 30 days. Our months are too long, so lunar phases drift earlier each month on our calendar, but the moon's phases remain fixed on a lunar calendar. The Hebrew calendar is a lunar calendar. Passover always is at full moon during the first month on this calendar. The reason that Passover (as well as Resurrection Sunday) bounce around on our calendar is that we don't follow a strictly lunar calendar.

Julius Caesar also instituted leap year. Since February was their catch-up month, that is where he placed leap day. As it turns out, the Julian calendar needed some improvements, so in 1582 many countries adopted the Gregorian calendar. That reform did several things, such as slightly alter the rule for leap day. More importantly, it moved New Year to January 1.

CHAPTER 3

The Solar System

> Level 1
> Level 2
> Level 3

MISSION LOG

SATELLITES
PLANET
MINOR PLANETS
NUCLEUS
ELLIPSE
COMA
ORBITAL PERIOD

The solar system consists of the sun and all the things that orbit it: planets and their satellites, asteroids, and comets. What is a planet? A planet is a large object that orbits the sun. Many thousands of things orbit the sun, but most of them are very small. So how large must a body be for us to call it a planet? Today, Mercury is the smallest planet, but from its discovery in 1930 until 2006 astronomers thought Pluto was the smallest planet. In 2006, astronomers decided that Pluto was too small to be a planet. If Pluto isn't a planet, what is it? Today we consider it an asteroid. While Pluto has more ice than most asteroids, asteroids far from the sun tend to have more ice.

Asteroids orbit the sun in orbits very similar to those of planets, but asteroids are far smaller than planets. Instead of calling them asteroids, astronomers prefer to use the term minor planets. When astronomers decided that Pluto no longer was a planet, they created a new classification for it and at least four other of the larger minor planets. We call Pluto, Eris, Ceres, Haumea, and Makemake "dwarf planets," but others likely will be added. Most minor planets are odd shaped, because they lack enough gravity to make themselves circular like the planets are. But dwarf planets are massive enough to have sufficient gravity so that they are round.

THE STARS OF HEAVEN

Genesis 2:1

Thus the heavens and the earth, and a the host of them, were finished.

Orbits of the Planets

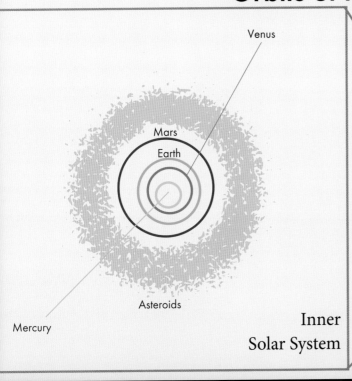

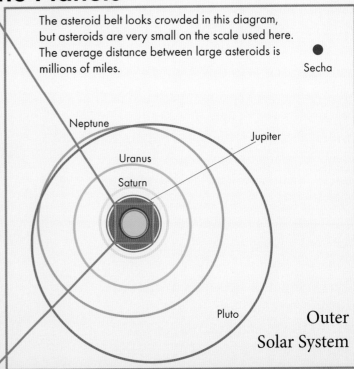

The asteroid belt looks crowded in this diagram, but asteroids are very small on the scale used here. The average distance between large asteroids is millions of miles.

Secha

Venus
Mars
Earth
Asteroids
Mercury

Inner Solar System

Neptune
Uranus
Saturn
Jupiter
Pluto

Outer Solar System

The orbits of the planets are nearly circles. The planets orbit the sun in the same direction. If we were to view the solar system from above the earth's North Pole, all the planets would orbit counterclockwise (CCW). Most of the planets rotate on their axes the same CCW direction. Most satellites orbit in the CCW direction, too. The orbits of all the planets lie in about the same plane. That means that the solar system is very flat. Minor planets are much smaller than planets, but they orbit the sun similar to the way planets do. That is, their orbits are nearly circular, they orbit the sun CCW, and their orbits are in about the same plane as the planets. That's why we call them minor planets.

Like minor planets, comets are very small, but their orbits are different from planets. First, their orbits are not circles. Instead, comet orbits are very long ellipses. An ellipse is sort of like a flattened circle. The sun is near one end of the ellipse, so comets spend much of the time far from the sun. Second, many comet orbits are tilted to the plane of the orbits of the planets. Third, while many comets orbit the sun CCW, nearly half orbit the sun clockwise (CW). For a long time, astronomers have thought that comets and minor planets were made of different material. Asteroids tend to be rocky, while comets have much ice. However, in recent years, astronomers have found that the composition of some minor planets more closely resemble the composition of comets.

The heart of a comet is its nucleus. A comet nucleus is mostly ice with a little rocky material. However, instead of being large particles, the rocky material in comets is in very small particles. Most of these particles are microscopic. We call the small particles dust. The dust mixed in with the ice makes the comet nucleus very dark. Astronomers sometimes call comet nuclei "dirty snowballs." Comet nuclei are very small, only a few kilometers across. The nuclei spend most of the time far, far from the sun where it is very cold. However, once each orbit, a comet nucleus comes very close to the sun. When this happens, the sun's light heats the ice so that it evaporates, and this knocks dust lose, too. The gas and dust expand to form a large cloud that we call the coma. A comet coma is many thousands of kilometers across. The coma glows because the sun's light excites the gas in a process that we call fluorescence. The sun's light also pushes the dust particles away from the sun to form a dust tail. The solar wind, an outrush of charged particles from the sun, blows the gas away from the sun, too. Therefore, a comet's tail always points away from the sun.

WONDER WHY?

What's in a name? There was a time in the past when people got to name any discoveries they made related to space. Ever wonder how modern discoveries of stars, planets, and planetary objects get their official names? Since 1919 the International Astronomical Union (IAU) has taken responsibility for overseeing this process. Naming can serve an important purpose — making it easier to keep track of features or celestial bodies rather than complex scientific designations by longitude and latitude. This is how Pluto's fourth and fifth moons became known as Kerberos and Styx.[5]

Confusion over the name of the moon is one reason for the founding of the IAU. Despite commercially-based offers for naming stars by a number of companies, none of these have anything to do with the actual official naming process of the IAU. Keeping the IAU method free of this commercial influence means that discoveries and planetary bodies can be identified in a uniform way, since often the public can also play a role in choosing names by voting. Even the naming of craters like those on Mars can include public input in cooperation with the IAU and international regulatory rules.[6]

Comets are very fragile. Every time a comet nucleus passes close to the sun, it loses much of its material, so after awhile, it gradually fades. Comets occasionally collide with planets. We saw this in 1994 when Comet Shoemaker-Levy IX plowed into Jupiter (image right). This destroyed the comet. Sometimes a comet passes close enough to a large planet, such as Jupiter, so that the planet's gravity kicks the comet out of the solar system, never to return. Astronomers have seen this many times. These three loss mechanisms — wearing out, collision with planets, and ejection from the solar system — tell us that comets cannot be billions of years old. Most astronomers think that the solar system is 4.6 billion years old, so how do they explain how we can have comets today?

How is a satellite different from a planet? A satellite orbits a planet. The earth has one natural satellite, the moon. Mercury and Venus have no satellites; Mars has only two very small satellites. Each of the other planets, Jupiter, Saturn, Uranus, and Neptune, has many satellites. In total, there are more than 150 satellites in the solar system. Most of the satellites are very small, but a few are large. Two satellites, Jupiter's Ganymede and Saturn's Titan (left, in front of Saturn's rings), are larger than Mercury, the smallest planet. Why are these two satellites not planets then? It is because they orbit a planet. Even though they are larger than the smallest planet, they are only satellites, because they orbit a planet rather than the sun.

Two Kinds of Planets

> Level 1
> Level 2
> Level 3

MISSION LOG

ASTRONOMICAL UNIT
MASS
DENSITY
ROTATION PERIODS
TERRESTRIAL
JOVIAN
GALILEAN SATELLITES
CRYOVOLCANISM

Planets are not all alike — but most known planets can be classified in two ways, but first you have to understand a little more about the planets themselves. The table on the next page has a list of properties of the eight planets. The first column gives the name of each planet, and the next column gives each planet's distance from the sun. The planets are very far from the sun, so miles or kilometers don't work very well. To make it easier, astronomers define a new unit of distance, the astronomical unit, or AU for short. The AU is the average distance between the earth and sun, so the earth is one AU from the sun.

The next column gives each planet's mass. Mass is the measurement of how much matter a body has. To make it simple, we've given the mass of the planets in terms of the earth's mass, so the earth has mass of one. The next column is diameter, again expressed in terms of the earth's diameter, so the earth's diameter is one. Next is density, expressed in grams/cubic centimeter. Density is a measure of how closely packed matter is. Density gives important clues about what something is made of. The last three columns give the rotation period of each planet, the number of satellites each planet has, and whether a planet has rings.

THE STARS OF HEAVEN

Psalm 8:3

When I consider Your heavens, the work of Your fingers,...

Planet		Distance from the sun (AU)	Mass	Diameter	Density	Rotation Period (Days)	Number of Satellites	Rings
Mercury		0.387	0.055	0.383	5.43	58.6	0	No
Venus		0.723	0.815	0.949	5.24	-243	0	No
Earth		1.000	1.000	1.000	5.515	0.997	1	No
Mars		1.52	0.107	0.533	3.94	1.03	2	No
Jupiter		5.20	318	11.2	1.33	0.414	16	Yes
Saturn		9.58	95.2	9.45	0.70	0.444	18	Yes
Uranus		19.3	14.5	4.01	1.30	-0.718	15	Yes
Neptune		30.2	17.2	3.88	1.76	0.671	8	Yes

We can see some interesting things in this table. First, notice that two planets, Venus and Uranus, have negative rotation periods. This means that they rotate backward (CW rather than CCW). Why do they do this? We don't really know.

Many astronomers think that the solar system is billions of years old and that the planets formed over a very long time. We call this belief evolution. Of course, the Bible tells us that God made the planets, along with the sun, moon, and stars, in just one day, the fourth day of the creation week. In addition, the Bible tells us that the creation was just a few thousand years ago, not billions of years ago. Many astronomers say that Venus and Uranus rotate backward, because very large objects hit them late during their formation and caused them to spin the wrong way. Such a thing should have altered their orbits around the sun from circles to be more elliptical, but Venus and Uranus have the most circular orbits of all the planets. This means that the collision idea probably is not true.

Another thing that we notice is that each of the planets easily falls into one of two groups. One group is the terrestrial planets, meaning earth-like. The terrestrial planets include the four planets closest to the sun — Mercury, Venus, Earth, and Mars. We call the outer four planets, Jupiter, Saturn, Uranus, and Neptune, the Jovian planets. Jovian means Jupiter-like. We can look at the table and see how the two types of planets are different. As already mentioned, the terrestrial planets are much closer to the sun than the Jovian planets are. The terrestrial planets also have far less mass and are much smaller than the Jovian planets. However, the terrestrial planets have more density than the Jovian planets. The Jovian planets rotate very quickly, while the terrestrial planets generally rotate slowly. The Jovian planets have many satellites, but the terrestrial planets have few, if any, satellites. Finally, all the Jovian planets have rings, but none of the terrestrial planets has rings.

Remember, density tells us something about what planets are made of. With their high density, the terrestrial planets are made of rocky material, so we frequently call them the rocky planets. The Jovian planets have too little density to be rocky, so we think that they contain much hydrogen and helium. Because hydrogen and helium are gases on Earth, we sometimes call the Jovian planets the gas giant planets. Evolutionists have a theory that they think explains how the planets gradually formed over time. This theory supposedly explains why the massive Jovian planets formed far from the sun while the small terrestrial planets formed close to the sun. However, in recent years, astronomers have found many extra-solar planets, planets orbiting other stars. Most of those planets are very massive like the Jovian planets, but they orbit very close to their stars, even closer than Mercury orbits the sun. According to the theory, those planets can't exist. This shows that the evolutionary theory is wrong and just how special the solar system is.

Why do the two types of planets have the properties that they have, properties such as their rotation rates, the number of satellites, and whether they have rings? That's not entirely clear, but with time, creation scientists may figure out the reasons why. Perhaps one day you may become an astronomer who believes in creation and helps to develop some of these ideas.

Remember earlier it was mentioned that Pluto is not considered a planet any longer? Besides being too small, another reason why Pluto isn't a planet anymore is that it doesn't fit in with the two types of planets. Being far from the sun, having low density, and having many satellites would make Pluto a Jovian planet. But Pluto's small mass and size, and its slow rotation rate argue for Pluto being a terrestrial planet. We don't know whether it has a ring system, but it probably doesn't.

Most minor planets are rocky, but the ones far from the sun appear to have more ice in them. This is generally true of small bodies far from the sun. For instance, many of the satellites of the Jovian planets contain much ice. We know this from their low density.

Mercury

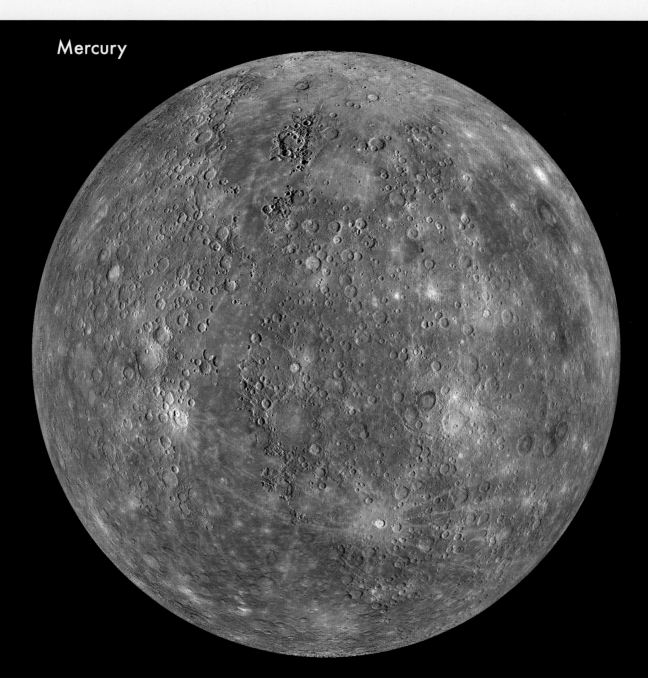

Mercury is a difficult planet to observe. From Earth, it never appears far from the sun, so we never see it in a dark sky, and it is very low in our sky so that our atmosphere blurs our view. Through a telescope it isn't much more than a small dot. We have sent two spacecraft to Mercury. They revealed that Mercury's surface has many craters.

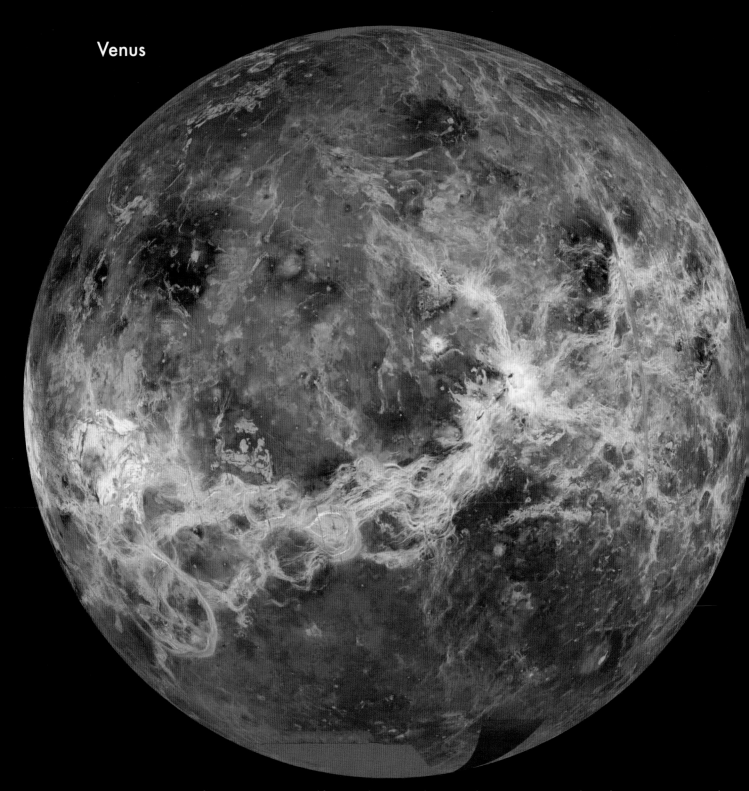

Venus

Astronomers sometimes refer to Venus as Earth's twin, because the two planets are so similar. They are more similar in size, mass, and density than any other planets. But the similarity ends there. The atmospheres of the two planets are very different. Venus's atmosphere is very cloudy, so we cannot see the surface of Venus. For a long time scientists thought that the clouds must be made of water droplets, as here on Earth. This suggested water on Venus, and the possibility of liquid water on Venus. Thus, people once thought that there might be life on Venus.

However, the clouds are made of droplets of sulfuric acid, not water. Venus' atmosphere is very thick and consists mostly of carbon dioxide (CO_2). CO_2 is a greenhouse gas, which means that it holds heat on the surface. The greenhouse effect allows some sunlight to reach the surface, and that sunlight heats the surface. The surface attempts to cool by radiating infrared radiation, but the greenhouse gas traps the infrared radiation, keeping the surface and lower atmosphere hot. Venus's very thick atmosphere means that its greenhouse effect is very efficient.

The surface temperature of Venus is about 900° F, day and night. This is hotter than the surface of Mercury, though Mercury is much closer to the sun. This obviously is hostile to life. The fact that Venus and Earth at first appear so similar but are so different shows us that it isn't easy for a planet to be a good environment for life.

While we can't penetrate the clouds of Venus visibly, we can "see" through it with radar, something that we've done with two spacecraft that have orbited the planet. This has allowed us to map most of its surface. The map reveals continent-like features on the surface, with mountains along some edges of the continents as on Earth. Keep in mind that though these features resemble continents, since there is no liquid water on Venus, there aren't any oceans.

There are some impact craters on Venus. The craters look very fresh, and they are sparsely spaced. This suggests that in the recent past, the surface of Venus was completely turned over in a catastrophic upheaval. Many models of the Flood suggest that the Flood was accompanied by geological upheaval. However, the same scientists who readily accept rapid upheaval on Venus reject the notion that something like that could have happened on Earth.

Mars

Mars is perhaps the most fascinating planet. We have sent many unmanned spacecraft to explore Mars. The earlier ones took photographs and measurements as they flew past Mars. Later spacecraft orbited the planet to take many more photographs and measurements. Eventually, we landed spacecraft on the Martian surface, and many of those were able to move around the surface. All of these missions have allowed us to learn much about Mars, and we have extensively mapped it.

There are regions of Mars that contain many craters, but there are other regions that contain few craters. There are two areas on the Martian surface that have volcanoes. Some of these volcanoes are huge, making them the largest volcanoes in the solar system. There also is a large crack running along the equator of Mars. This deep canyon is as long as the United States is wide.

For many years people thought that life might exist on Mars. Now we know that Mars is hostile to life, but most scientists recognize that it is the least hostile to life of all the planets other than the earth. Therefore, there is continued hope despite strong evidence to the contrary that life either exists on Mars today or did once in the past. Mars has polar ice caps (image below) that are visible in telescopes on Earth. That suggests perhaps liquid water might exist on Mars. It is true that there is water ice on Mars, but the temperature and atmospheric pressure on Mars are far too low for liquid water to exist on Mars today. However, there are many river channels on the Martian surface. In addition, there appear to be shorelines high on the sides of hills that suggest that there once was water to considerable depth on Mars.

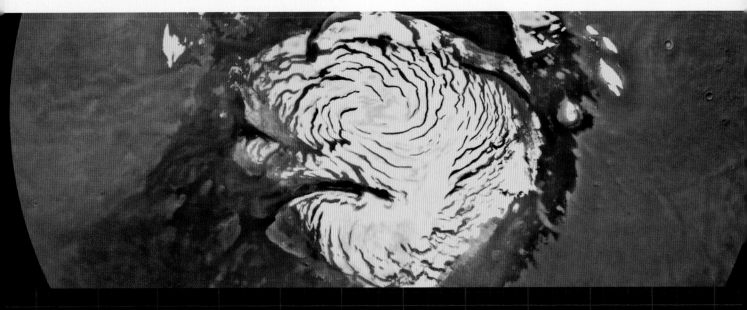

Apparently, Mars once had a more extensive atmosphere and was much wetter and warmer than today. What happened to all that water? What happened to the atmosphere on Mars? The gravity there is far too weak to hold onto an atmosphere, so as the atmosphere bled away, the water soon evaporated and followed, though there may be much frozen water in the rocks and soils. The main mystery is how Mars acquired an atmosphere in the first place. Perhaps God made Mars with an atmosphere, but the planet lost it.

It is interesting that many planetary scientists think that Mars once had a global or near-global flood. This is on a planet that has no liquid water today and perhaps very little water at all. Yet, these same scientists don't think that such a thing could have happened on Earth where we have plenty of water.

Jupiter

Jupiter is well-known for the banded structure and Great Red Spot in its atmosphere. We have sent five spacecraft to Jupiter. Their cameras and other instruments have allowed us to learn much more about Jupiter than we could have using telescopes on Earth alone. Of particular interest are the Galilean satellites, the four largest moons of Jupiter. We call them the Galilean satellites, because Galileo discovered them with his telescope. In fact, he used them as an example of how the planets orbited the sun.

Io, the innermost Galilean satellite, is the only body with a solid surface in the solar system that does not have impact craters. This is because it is geologically active, with many volcanoes erupting at any given time. In fact, we have photographs of some of them erupting. The volcanoes quickly cover any craters that might form. However, the molten material on Io is sulfur, not rock as here on Earth.

Europa, the second Galilean satellite, is covered with a thick layer of ice. Europa probably has a rocky core. Many astronomers think that there is a liquid water region between the rocky core and the icy surface. If so, they hope that life might exist in that subsurface ocean, but that is very unlikely.

Saturn

We have visited Saturn with four robotic spacecraft. Saturn is famous for its grand ring system made of many small particles of ice and rock. There are many gaps in the ring system, with the largest visible with telescopes on the earth. The rings are caused by the gravitational pull of Saturn's many satellites. These little tugs and other forces rapidly tear apart the ring system, so we know that the rings cannot last very long. This shows that the rings of Saturn and the other Jovian planets cannot be billions of years old.

Beside its rings, Saturn has many satellites. Titan, Saturn's largest satellite, is the only satellite with an atmosphere. Titan's atmosphere has one similarity to Earth's atmosphere — both primarily are nitrogen, but the similarity ends there. Titan is very cold. The clouds appear to be made of droplets of methane. On Earth, methane is natural gas. There are pools of methane on Titan's surface, but this cannot happen on Earth, because Earth is far too warm.

Mimas, another satellite of Saturn, has a large impact crater that we call Herschel, named after Frederick William Herschel, the man who discovered Uranus. Herschel is so large that it is not clear how it formed without destroying Mimas. Another satellite, Iapetus, has one side that is very dark and the other side that is very light.

Uranus

Neptune

We have visited Uranus and Neptune with only one spacecraft, and it merely flew past either planet as it took photographs and made measurements. Uranus is very strange in that the entire system is tilted nearly on its side so that it rotates almost perpendicular to its revolution.

Uranus is green, and even appears as a green dot in a large telescope. Neptune appears as a blue dot in large telescopes. Neptune has the Great Dark Spot in its atmosphere. Apparently, both it and Jupiter's Great Red Spot are large storms in the atmospheres of their respective planets.

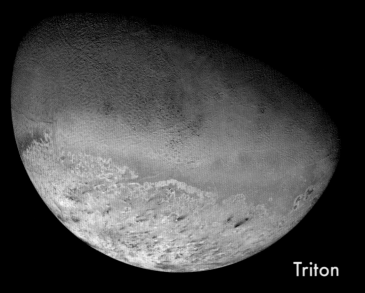

Triton

One of Neptune's satellites, **Triton**, is volcanically active. However, the molten material here probably is water, rather than rock. Objects as far as Triton is from the sun are very cold, so liquid water is hot material for them. Planetary scientists call the volcanic activity on Triton cryovolcanism, meaning very cold volcanism. Cryovolcanism has altered Triton's surface so that it has an appearance that resembles a cantaloupe.

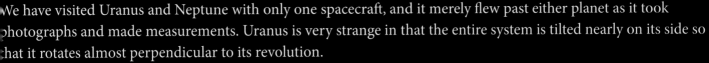

The Sun

> Level 1
> Level 2
> Level 3

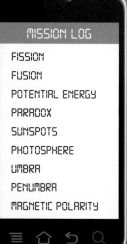

MISSION LOG

FISSION

FUSION

POTENTIAL ENERGY

PARADOX

SUNSPOTS

PHOTOSPHERE

UMBRA

PENUMBRA

MAGNETIC POLARITY

The sun is a large, hot ball of gas. The sun is 109 times larger than the earth. If you wanted to make a model of the solar system, you could make the sun the size of a basketball. On this scale, the earth would be about the size of a BB, about one-tenth of an inch (2.5 mm) across. This little BB would orbit the sun 100 feet (30 meters) away. The sun is so large that more than a million earths would fit inside.

We know that God made the sun (the greater light) on the fourth day, along with the moon (the lesser light) and the stars. Since the planets appear as stars in our sky, God made them on day 4 as well. However, God created light on day 1, so where did the light come from for the first three days, before there was a sun? We don't know, because God has not told us. Some people have suggested that since in the future New Jerusalem we will have no need of the light of the sun or the moon, because God will be the light in that city (Revelation 21:23), that God was the source of light for the first three days. That is a good idea, but we don't know for sure if that is correct. All that would be necessary for day and night is a light source and a rotating earth.

Only a very tiny portion of the sun's light falls on the earth, so the sun provides a huge amount of energy every moment. What is the source of the sun's energy? We think that the sun is nuclear powered. On earth, a nuclear power plant operates by fission. Fission is a process where a large atom, such as uranium, fissions, or breaks, into smaller atoms. Fission releases much energy. However, the sun operates by fusion. Fusion is the opposite of fission. Instead of breaking large atoms into smaller ones, fusion combines smaller atoms into larger atoms. In the sun, fusion combines hydrogen atoms into helium atoms. This fusion releases even more energy than fission does. The sun could shine for billions of years with fusion.

THE STARS OF HEAVEN

Psalm 74:16

The day is Yours, the night also is Yours; You have prepared the light and the sun.

A long time ago, astronomers thought that the sun got its power from gravitational potential energy. In this process, the sun slowly shrinks to release energy. However, this process is not nearly as efficient as fusion, so the sun could shine using this energy source for only a few tens of millions of years. Scientists who believed in evolution realized that this was not nearly enough time for evolution to have happened, but it would have been no problem if God recently created the world. In 1979, two astronomers thought that they found evidence that the sun was shrinking, but this turned out to be wrong. Unfortunately, many creationists thought that this proved that the sun got its energy from gravity and so proved that the sun was not billions of years old. Some creationists still use this to show that the sun is very young sun, but this is not a good argument.

However, all is not well with an old sun. If the sun gets its energy from nuclear fusion, then over billions of years, the sun ought to get brighter. As the sun brightens, the earth would heat up tremendously, and this would make life on earth very difficult, if not impossible. Starting from the temperatures that exist on earth today, if the sun is billions of years old, then the earth would have been far colder in the past. However, no one believes that the earth once was much colder than it is today. If the sun and earth are billions of years old, how has the earth maintained the same average temperature? Evolutionary scientists call this the young faint sun paradox. Those scientists have proposed various solutions to prevent the earth from heating over billions of years, but those solutions don't work. However, if the sun is not billions of years old, but only thousands of years old, as creationists believe, then this is not a problem.

The sun is very bright, and it will damage your eyes if you look directly at it. There are some safe ways to look at the sun, but you should never attempt that unless you know what you are doing. It is best to have an adult that knows how to safely look at the sun to show you what the sun looks like. Even though the sun is gas, it appears to have a surface. Astronomers call this surface the photosphere. The photosphere is the part of the sun from which we receive almost all the sun's radiation.

The photosphere sometimes has spots on it. We call these sunspots. Sunspots look dark, but they actually are very bright, too bright to look at with the unaided eye. How can that be? Sunspots are not as hot as the surrounding photosphere, so they look dimmer than the rest of the photosphere. Sunspots have a darker inner region that we call the umbra. The less-dark outer region is the penumbra. A sunspot normally will last a few days or a few weeks. They often appear to change noticeably from day to day. We use sunspots to time how long it takes the sun to rotate. The sun's rotation period is about a month, so not only do we see changes in sunspots themselves from day to day, but also spots appear to move each day due to the sun's rotation.

The number of sunspots changes over about an 11-year cycle. We call this the sunspot cycle. During sunspot minimum, the sun may not have any spots for months. During sunspot maximum, the sun will have several spots nearly every day. The last sunspot maximum was in 2013. This will allow you to calculate when future sunspots are likely to occur. Sunspots normally appear in pairs, with the pairs lined up parallel to the equator. Sunspots are regions of strong magnetic fields on the sun. The spots in a pair have opposite magnetic polarity — one spot is a north magnetic pole, and the other spot is a south magnetic pole.

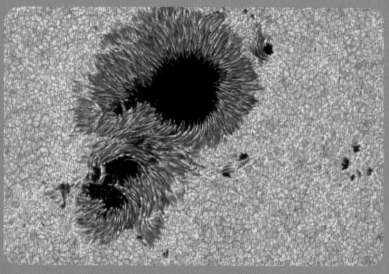

Granule-like structure of surface of sun and sunspots

Our Sun

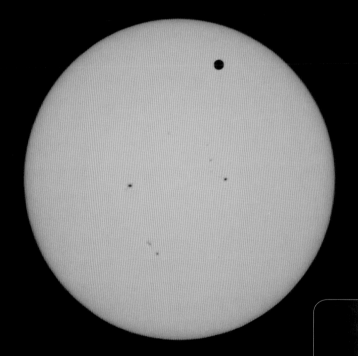

The sun with sunspots. The round dot is Venus passing directly in front of the sun as seen from Earth. Transits of Venus like this are relatively rare. This one happened in 2012. The next one won't be until the year 2117.

During sunspot maximum, there is much magnetic activity on the sun. This magnetic activity can produce flares on the sun. A solar flare releases much energy into space, but most of the radiation is invisible to the eye. A solar flare also releases many charged particles. These charged particles amount to a gust in the solar wind. These charged particles are moving very fast, and they take a day or two to reach the earth.

The charged particles interact with the earth's magnetic field to cause magnetic storms. Magnetic storms can interrupt electronic communications. They also can cause an aurora as the charged particles strike atoms high in the earth's atmosphere. Aurorae more often are called northern lights, at least in the Northern Hemisphere, because you generally see them in the northern part of the sky. In the Southern Hemisphere, people call aurorae the southern lights.

Telescopes

> Level 1
> Level 2
> Level 3

Astronomers use telescopes to study things in the sky. There are two basic types of telescopes — refractors and reflectors. A refracting telescope uses a lens to refract, or bend, light to form an image. At the other end of the telescope, there is an eyepiece used to view and magnify the image. Instead of a lens, a reflecting telescope uses a concave mirror to form the image. Since the light reflects back toward the direction that it came in, a reflecting telescope usually has a second, small mirror to send the light out the side of the telescope.

How do we measure the size of a telescope? We measure the size by the diameter of the lens or mirror. The bigger that lens or mirror is, the more light that the telescope collects. Things appear brighter in a larger telescope. Things far away appear very dim, so larger telescopes allow us to see farther into space. The largest refracting telescope is the 40-inch telescope at Yerkes Observatory in Williams Bay, Wisconsin. The largest reflecting telescopes are the twin ten-meter Keck telescopes at Mauna Kea Observatory in Hawaii. The largest telescopes tend to be reflectors, because they are easier and less expensive to make than refractors are.

MISSION LOG

SPECTROGRAPH
WAVELENGTHS
ELECTROMAGNETIC &
INFRARED RADIATION
MICROWAVES
RADIO WAVES
SPECTROSCOPY
SPECTRAL LINES
DOPPLER EFFECT

THE STARS OF HEAVEN

Psalm 19:1

*The heavens declare
the glory of God;
And the firmament shows
His handiwork.*

Telescopes are fun to look through, but when doing research, astronomers rarely actually look through their telescopes. Instead, they attach special instruments to the telescopes. Sometimes the instrument is a very special electronic camera that takes photographs. Astronomers can examine the structure of astronomical bodies on the pictures, or they might measure how bright the stars are on the images.

Many stars change brightness, and studying how those stars change allows astronomers to better understand those stars. Other times, an astronomer might use a spectrograph. A spectrograph divides light up into its wavelengths. Light is a wave, and wavelength is how long the wave is. In visible light, we see longer wavelengths as red, and we see shorter wavelengths as blue or violet. We can describe the colors of the spectrum in order of decreasing wavelength as ROYGBIV, where R = red, O = orange, Y = yellow, G = green, B = blue, I = indigo, and V = violet.

R	O	Y	G	B	I	V
red	orange	yellow	green	blue	indigo	violet

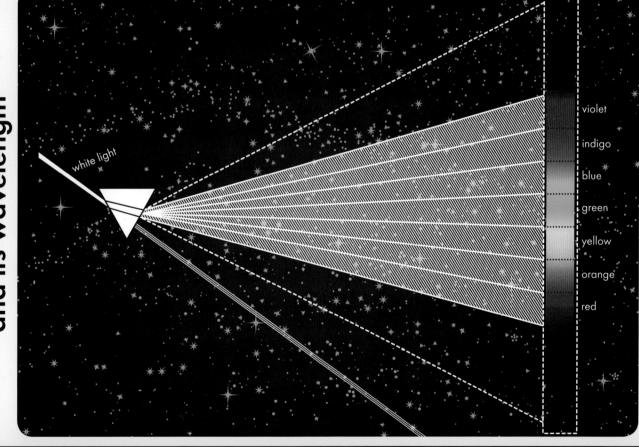

Spectrum of white light and its wavelength

white light

violet
indigo
blue
green
yellow
orange
red

There are many other wavelengths beyond what we can see with our eyes. We generally think of light as being visible, so it's best to call these other, invisible wavelengths, electromagnetic radiation. At wavelengths too short for our eyes to see is ultraviolet light. Wavelengths that are shorter than ultraviolet are X-rays, and beyond X-rays are gamma rays. These wavelengths of electromagnetic radiation shorter than what the eye can see are harmful to living things, but in His provision for us, God designed the earth's atmosphere to block most of these. While this is good for us, it makes astronomy difficult, because these short-wavelength radiations blocked by the earth's atmosphere contain information that we can use to study astronomical bodies. We solve this problem by launching special telescopes in orbit around the earth above the earth's atmosphere or by launching balloons to high altitude.

Infrared radiation has wavelengths longer than what is visible to the eye. While you can't see infrared, you can feel it radiating from a hot object. This is why we call infrared "heat radiation." At even longer wavelengths are microwaves, and beyond them are radio waves. The earth's atmosphere blocks much of the infrared and some of the microwave, so astronomers reach those wavelengths with orbiting telescopes or balloons, too. However, most radio waves come through the earth's atmosphere, so astronomers can study those from the ground. Radio astronomers use large dish-shaped telescopes to receive radio waves. These look like very large satellites dishes. Some are very large — more than 100 meters. Radio astronomers frequently connect many radio telescopes to improve the performance of their instruments.

Spectroscopy is the study of spectra. The spectra of many astronomical bodies have dark or bright emission lines. Different elements produce different spectral lines, so astronomers can use the spectral lines to determine the composition of astronomical bodies. However, which spectral lines are present also depends upon temperature, so astronomers can use them to measure temperature. Other factors can alter spectral lines. For instance, strong magnetic fields can cause spectral lines to split, so we can use the amount of splitting to measure magnetic fields. This is how we know that sunspots are regions of strong magnetic fields. If an object is moving toward or away from us, its spectral lines shift from their normal wavelengths. We call this the Doppler Effect, after Christian Doppler, the man who discovered this principle. The amount of Doppler shift depends on how fast an object is moving, so we can use the Doppler shift to measure the speeds of astronomical bodies.

An antennae dish at the Very Large Array shown in scale to a person.

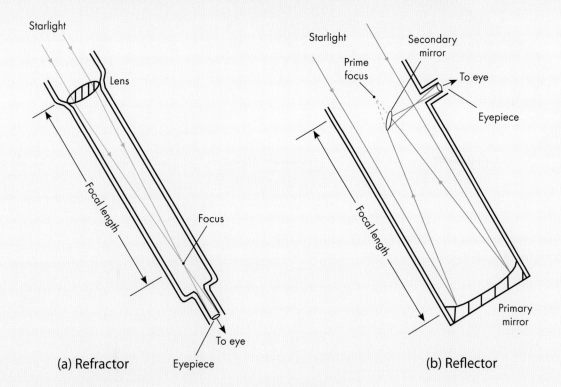

Starlight

Lens

Focal length

Focus

To eye

Eyepiece

(a) Refractor

Starlight

Prime focus

Secondary mirror

To eye

Eyepiece

Focal length

Primary mirror

(b) Reflector

Refractors and Reflectors Comparison of (a) refracting and (b) reflecting telescopes. Both types are used to gather and focus electromagnetic radiation — to be observed by human eyes or recorded on photographs or in computers. In both cases, the image formed at the focus is viewed with a small magnifying lens called an eyepiece.

WONDER WHY?

Hubble Trouble Means a New Eye in the Sky Since 1996, scientists and technicians from over 15 countries have been collaborating on the development of the James Webb Space Telescope as a successor to the Hubble Space Telescope that was originally launched in 1990 and will end up falling back to Earth in a decade or so, having lasted much longer than the United States space shuttle program, which was utilized in servicing the telescope.[7]

Despite cost and time overruns for the project, work continues trying to achieve a revised 2018 launch date, having run at least seven years behind on its schedule. The telescope will feature a number of advancements to offer exciting new opportunities to see faint, distant objects with its gold-coated mirror segments and will include sunshield protection.[8]

The James Webb Space Telescope will have an orbit of 940,000 miles (1.5 million km) from Earth, again taking current technology to its limits as it peers at the deepest recesses of space.[9]

A James Webb Space Telescope primary mirror segment, coated with gold.

Six of the James Webb Space Telescope beryllium mirror segments undergoing a series of cryogenic tests.

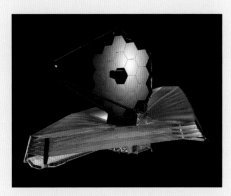

Illustration of the James Webb Space Telescope, view from the top (opposite side from the sun).

History of Astronomy

CHAPTER 7

> Level 1
> Level 2
> Level 3

MISSION LOG

PARALLAX
GEOCENTRIC THEORY
HELIOCENTRIC THEORY
EPICYCLE
RETROGRADE
LAWS OF PLANETARY
    MOTION
PHYSICS

Learning about the universe is not a modern study. Many ancient civilizations studied the stars trying to discover their secrets. For instance, the ancient Greeks were very good astronomers.

Many of them made amazing discoveries. For instance, by 500 B.C. they had figured out that the earth was round, like a ball. They reached this conclusion several ways. As we saw earlier, one way they learned this was by looking at the moon during a lunar eclipse. A lunar eclipse happens when the earth's shadow falls on the moon. The earth's shadow always was a circle. The only shape in three dimensions that always casts a circular shadow is a sphere. Another way that the ancient Greeks knew that the earth was spherical was by watching how high in the sky stars appear as one travels north and south. As you travel northward, stars in the north get higher in the sky while stars in the south get lower. The reverse happens as you travel southward. This can happen only if the earth is spherical.

Not only did the ancient Greeks know that the earth was a sphere, but one accurately measured the earth's size. Around 200 B.C., Eratosthenes measured how high in the sky the sun was at noon at two locations on the same date. He chose the date of the summer solstice, but, since he couldn't instantly travel between the two locations, he made his measurements in two different years. The two locations were along a north-south line, and knowing the distance between the two locations and the difference in the height of the sun at the two locations, Eratosthenes used math to find the circumference of the earth. His result was accepted until just a few hundred years ago. However, his measurement is very close to the actual size of the earth.

THE STARS OF HEAVEN

Job 22:12

Is not God in the height of heaven?
And see the highest stars,
how lofty they are!

The ancient Greeks also noticed that the sun appeared to move once around through the stars each year. In fact, this is the definition of the year. The ancient Greeks realized that either the sun moved around the earth each year or the earth moved around the sun, but which was true? They knew that if the earth moved around the sun each year, our changing position ought to make us see the stars in a slightly different direction. That is, the stars ought to shift slightly back and forth each year as we orbit the sun. We call this effect parallax.

You can demonstrate parallax by holding one thumb up at arm's length, and then view your thumb with one eye and then the other. Your thumb will appear to shift back and forth. Imagine that your thumb is a star, and that one of your eyes is on one side of the earth's orbit, while the other eye is on the other side, with the sun in between your eyes. The ancient Greeks looked for parallax, but they never saw it. Therefore, being good scientists, they concluded that the earth did not orbit the sun.

Distant stars

Near star parallax motion

p

Parallax angle

Near star

Earth's motion around sun

We call the belief that the earth remains motionless while the sun orbits it the geocentric theory. Geocentric means "earth centered." Today we know that the earth is just one of eight planets orbiting the sun. We call this the heliocentric theory, meaning "sun centered." Most ancient people believed the geocentric theory, though a few chose to believe in the heliocentric theory. How did those few ancients who believed the heliocentric theory explain the lack of parallax? They argued that the stars were so far away that parallax was too small to be visible. It turns out, they were right. You can show that parallax is less for objects that are more distant. Try asking a friend to stand some distance away with his thumb held up. You will see if you repeat the parallax experiment with either eye that the shift is not nearly as great. The closest star is so far away that the parallax shift is the same angle that you would see if you looked at a dime from three kilometers. The first parallax measurements were not until the 1830s.

The ancient Greeks thought that heavenly bodies were perfect and hence must follow perfect rules. The perfect rules were that astronomical objects must move along circles at a constant rate. These rules were easy enough to explain the daily spinning of the entire sky due to the earth's rotation on its axis. The sky just simply turned once per day. These perfect rules even could explain the sun's motion each year and the moon's motion each month, though not perfectly. However, the perfect rules could not easily explain the retrograde motion of the planets with the geocentric theory. Around A.D. 140, a Greek astronomer named Ptolemy figured out a way to do this. He had each planet move along a smaller circle that then moved along a larger circle. He called the smaller circle an *epicycle*. Whenever the planet was near its closest point to the earth on its epicycle, the planet appeared to

opernicus Monument in Warsaw

move retrograde. By adjusting the sizes of the circles and the speeds, he was able to explain the motions of planets well. He did have to add another small epicycle for each planet to account for the slight bobbing up and down that the planets do because their orbits are not exactly in the same orbital plane of the earth. He also had to add a small epicycle satisfactorily to explain the moon's motion and another small one for the sun.

There were two more necessary refinements. First, the earth was not exactly at the center, but was displaced a short distance from the center. Second, the epicycle did not move at a constant rate with respect to the earth or even the center of the deferent, but with respect to another point called the equant.

With these adjustments, Ptolemy's theory worked well for fifteen hundred years. Along the way, astronomers had to add additional epicycles to make the theory match the real world. By the year 1600, some versions of Ptolemy's theory required the use of more than one hundred epicycles. As you can imagine, this was very complicated. In 1543, Nicolaus Copernicus published a book where he argued that the heliocentric theory was much simpler, and hence probably was right. Many people think that Copernicus invented the heliocentric theory, but this is not correct, because there were ancient astronomers who taught this theory. Still, Copernicus's book was very influential, and in his book, he determined the sizes of the orbits of the five known planets in AU and determined their true orbital periods. No one had done this before.

The basic elements of Ptolemaic astronomy, showing a planet on an epicycle (smaller dashed circle), a deferent (larger dashed circle), the eccentric (X) and an equant (larger black dot).

The phases of Venus, observed by Galileo in 1610

Galileo Galilei read Copernicus' book, and he was convinced that the heliocentric theory was true. Galileo made many important contributions to science, but his most important one was the use of the telescope. Galileo did not invent the telescope, but he was the first to use it to view astronomical bodies. He discovered several things that challenged the scientific thinking of the day. For instance, he saw that Venus went through phases similar to the moon. This can happen only if Venus orbits the sun. This directly disproved the geocentric theory of Ptolemy, because in Ptolemy's theory, no planet could orbit the sun. Galileo saw craters on the moon and spots on the sun. But the predominant teaching at the time was that the sun and moon were perfect, so they could not have such blemishes. Galileo also saw four satellites orbiting the planet Jupiter. He argued that these much smaller satellites orbited larger Jupiter in much the same way that the much smaller planets orbited the much larger sun.

About the same time as Galileo was doing his work, Johannes Kepler read Copernicus's book, and he too became convinced that the heliocentric theory was true. Kepler studied observations of planetary positions that Tycho Brahe, another astronomer, had made over about 20 years. Kepler attempted to make sense of the data in terms of the heliocentric theory. Along the way, he discovered three laws of planetary motion.

About 50 years later, Sir Isaac Newton was able develop the science of physics. He developed his law of gravity by studying the moon's motion around the earth. When Newton applied his new physics to the planets, he was able to show better how Kepler's three laws worked. At this time, science began to develop, and especially astronomy and physics. This led to what we now consider modern times.

Replica of Isaac Newton's second reflecting telescope of 1672.

Kennedy Launches the Moon Race!

Kennedy announced his support for the Apollo program on May 25, 1961, and redefined the ultimate goal of the Space Race in an address to a special joint session of Congress: "I believe that this nation should commit itself to achieving the goal, before this decade is out, of landing a man on the moon and returning him safely to the earth." He expressed his reasoning in his "We choose to go to the Moon" speech, on 12 September 1962, before a large crowd at Rice University Stadium, in Houston, Texas, near the site of the future Johnson Space Center.[10]

Chronology of U.S. Astronaut Missions (1961 – 1972)

1961
Mercury Redstone 3 - May 5, 1961 - Earth Suborbital
Mercury Redstone 4 - July 21, 1961 - Earth Suborbital

1962
Mercury Atlas 6 - February 20, 1962 - Earth Orbiter
Mercury Atlas 7 - May 24, 1962 - Earth Orbiter
Mercury Atlas 8 - October 3, 1962 - Earth Orbiter

1963
Mercury Atlas 9 - May 15, 1963 - Earth Orbiter

1965
Gemini 3 - March 23, 1965 - Earth Orbiter
Gemini 4 - June 3, 1965 - Earth Orbiter
Gemini 5 - August 21, 1965 - Earth Orbiter
Gemini 7 - December 4, 1965 - Earth Orbiter
Gemini 6A - December 15, 1965 - Earth Orbiter

1966
Gemini 8 - March 16, 1966 - Earth Orbiter
Gemini 9A - June 3, 1966 - Earth Orbiter
Gemini 10 - July 18, 1966 - Earth Orbiter
Gemini 11 - September 12, 1966 - Earth Orbiter
Gemini 12 - November 11, 1966 - Earth Orbiter

1968
Apollo 7 - October 11, 1968 - Earth Orbiter
Apollo 8 - December 21, 1968 - Lunar Orbiter

1969
Apollo 9 - March 3, 1969 - Earth Orbiter
Apollo 10 - May 18, 1969 - Lunar Orbiter
Apollo 11 - July 16, 1969 - Lunar Landing
Apollo 12 - November 14, 1969 - Lunar Landing

1970
Apollo 13 - April 11, 1970 - Lunar Mission - Landing Aborted

1971
Apollo 14 - January 31, 1971 - Lunar Landing
Apollo 15 - July 26, 1971 - Lunar Landing

1972
Apollo 16 - April 16, 1972 - Lunar Landing
Apollo 17 - December 7, 1972 - Lunar Landing

http://en.wikipedia.org/wiki/Project_Mercury
http://en.wikipedia.org/wiki/Project_Gemini
http://en.wikipedia.org/wiki/Apollo_program

CHAPTER 8

Stars

> **Level 1**
> **Level 2**
> **Level 3**

MISSION LOG

LIGHT YEARS

ABSOLUTE MAGNITUDE

PARSEC

BINARY SYSTEMS

WHITE DWARF STARS

NEUTRON STAR

BLACK HOLE

SUPERNOVAE

PULSAR

As we have already learned, the stars are very far away. Today we think of the sun as being a star. However, in ancient times people thought that the sun was very different from the stars. This was because the sun is so much brighter than the stars. While the sun is of above-average brightness, the only reason the stars appear so faint compared to the sun is that they are so far way. Astronomers sometimes express the distances of stars in light years. The light year is the distance that light travels in a year. The closest star is a little more than four light years away. Many of the brighter stars at night are dozens, or even hundreds, of light years away. A few are even a few thousand light years away.

Astronomers have different ways of measuring the distances to the stars. The most direct way is by use of parallax. As we have already seen, parallax decreases with increasing distance. Astronomers use a type of math called trigonometry to use this fact to find the distances of stars. This method of parallax works out to distances of several hundred light years, but with improved technology this likely will increase to thousands of light years soon.

It is obvious to anyone who has looked at the night sky that stars have different brightness. The ancient Greeks developed *magnitudes*, a system for measuring star brightness. We still use this system today. The brightest-appearing stars in the sky are first magnitude. Stars a bit fainter than first magnitude are second magnitude. The North Star and the stars in the belt of Orion are second magnitude. The magnitude numbers continue to increase as stars get fainter. The faintest stars visible to the naked eye on a very clear, dark night are about magnitude six.

THE STARS OF HEAVEN

Job 38:7

When the morning stars sang together, and all the sons of God shouted for joy?

However, we continue the magnitude system to stars much fainter than what we can see with the eye alone. The faintest stars now detected with our largest telescopes are about magnitude 30. There are a few stars and other objects a little brighter than first magnitude. The brightest appearing star in the sky is Sirius, the Dog Star. It is magnitude -1.4. Jupiter appears as a bright star of magnitude -2.2. But the brightest appearing "star" is Venus at -4.4 at brightest. The full moon is -12, and the sun is -26.

The bright star Sirius is a binary star, which means that it consists of two stars orbiting one another because of their mutual gravity. The brighter star in the system is called Sirius A, and the fainter one is called Sirius B. This is an artist's impression of Sirius A and Sirius B. Sirius A is the larger of the two stars.

What we have described here is apparent magnitude, how bright a star appears to us. But does a bright star appear bright because it really is bright, or because it happens to be very close to us? Imagine a nightlight and an automobile headlight. It is obvious that the headlight is brighter. However, if the headlight was far away and the nightlight was close by, the nightlight might appear brighter. To express how bright stars actually are, imagine moving all the stars to the same standard distance. Nearby stars then would appear fainter than they normally do, while faraway stars would appear brighter.

Astronomers choose the standard distance to be 10 parsecs. A parsec is 3.26 light years, so 10 parsecs is 32.6 light years. The absolute magnitude is how bright a star would be if it were at the standard distance of 10 parsecs. The sun's absolute magnitude is 4.6. Though you can see a 4.6 magnitude star on a clear, dark night, it would not appear very bright. And if the sky is bright because of city lights or a full moon, you probably couldn't see a 4.6 magnitude star with your eyes alone.

Stars also have different colors. Color tells us the temperatures of stars. Astronomers normally use the Kelvin scale to express temperature (abbreviated K). Kelvin is on the Celsius scale, but has no negative temperatures. Instead of starting with zero at the freezing point of water, the Kelvin scale has zero at absolute zero, the coldest possible temperature. Since absolute zero is -273 C, you convert from Celsius to Kelvin by adding 273 (and you subtract 273 to convert Kelvin to Celsius). The coolest stars are about 3,000 K, and the hottest are about 100,000 K. The sun's temperature is about 6,000 K. This makes the sun and similar temperature stars appear yellow. The coolest stars look red, while stars in between are orange. On the other hand, stars warmer than the sun are white or even blue.

As we previously mentioned, the lines visible in the spectrum of a star depend upon both temperature and composition. The most common element in the universe is hydrogen, and so stars normally contain much hydrogen. However, the hottest stars are too hot for hydrogen lines to appear in their spectra. In addition, cooler stars are too cool for hydrogen lines to be in their spectra either. Stars that have the strongest hydrogen lines have temperature of about 10,000 K. Stars cooler than this, such as the sun, have weak hydrogen lines. To determine stellar composition, astronomers must carefully consider temperature. Astronomers classify spectra according to the spectral lines that they see, but the system is primarily about temperature. Starting with the hottest stars and progressing to the coolest stars, the spectral types are O, B, A, F, G, K, and M. Astronomers also have subtypes from 0 to 9 within each spectral type. For instance, the sun is a G2 star. A0 stars have the strongest hydrogen lines.

BB

Not only do stars have different temperatures and brightness, but they come in different sizes, too. The sun's diameter is more than one hundred times the diameter of the earth. If the sun were the size of a basketball, the earth would be the size of a BB. Astronomers group the sun with most stars in what they call the "main sequence." You can think of these as being normal stars. The smallest main sequence stars are about one-tenth the size of the sun, while the largest main sequence stars are about ten times larger than the sun.

Stars frequently occur in binary systems. The word *binary* means "two," so a binary star is a system of two stars orbiting one another. This is similar to a planet orbiting the sun. The difference is that the sun has far more mass than the planets do, but stars in binary systems frequently have similar mass. Since the sun has so much more mass than the planets, the planets move quite a bit, but the sun hardly moves. On the other hand, since stars in a binary system have such similar mass, both stars noticeably move. The study of binary stars is very important. How fast the stars move depends upon the gravity, but the gravity depends upon the stars' masses. Therefore, by studying binary stars, astronomers can find how much mass stars have.

How do astronomers measure the sizes of stars? There are several ways, but the most direct way is to study a certain type of binary stars. A binary star is a system of two stars orbiting one another by their mutual gravity. Sometimes we view a binary star along the plane of the orbits of the stars. When this happens, the stars block each other's light once per orbit. This is a sort of an eclipse, so we call these systems eclipsing binary stars. By timing how long the eclipses last, astronomers can directly measure how large the stars are. Binary stars are involved in many processes that astronomers are very interested in.

Extreme Stars Beyond the main sequence there are some large extremes in the sizes of stars. On one extreme are giant and supergiant stars. The largest ones are a thousand times larger than the sun. If we were to replace the sun with one of the supergiant stars, some of the planets, including the earth, would orbit inside the star! Because of their large size, giant stars are very thin. Many of them would be less dense than the air that we breathe.

On the other extreme of size are white dwarf stars. They are much smaller than the sun, about the size of the earth. We call them white dwarfs because they are hot enough to be white, and they are so small. While white dwarfs are very small, they have mass that is close to that of the sun. That means that the matter in a white dwarf is packed very tightly. If you could bring a teaspoon of a white dwarf to the earth, it might weigh as much an automobile! These stars are very strange, but astronomers think that they understand a lot about them.

White Dwarf Star

Sirius, the brightest star in our sky, has a binary companion that is a white dwarf. The bright star in the center is Sirius, while the faint star to the lower left is the white dwarf.

There is a maximum mass that a white dwarf can have. That maximum is about 1.4 times the mass of the sun. If a star is as small as a white dwarf but has more mass than this, it becomes an even stranger star called a *neutron star*. However, neutron stars are far smaller than white dwarfs, less than one-thousandth the size of the earth. This is about the size of a large city. Neutron stars typically have 2 to 3 times the mass of the sun. To pack all that matter into such a small space must make

neutron stars very dense. If you brought a teaspoon of a neutron star to the earth, it would weigh more than all the automobiles ever manufactured! It is hard to imagine something like this. What is the matter in a neutron star like? The matter of a neutron star is not like ordinary matter on the earth. Instead of being in the form of atoms made of protons, electrons, and neutrons, neutron stars are made of neutrons. The neutrons are arranged into one mass, sort of like a giant atomic nucleus.

Artist concept illustrates jets of material shooting out from the neutron star in the binary system 4U 0614+091

Being so small, neutron stars are very faint, usually too faint for us to see, even with large telescopes. However, neutron stars spin very rapidly. They also have very strong magnetic fields. As a neutron stars spins, its powerful magnetic field spins as well. The moving magnetic field causes charged particles nearby to emit powerful radiation along a beam. As the neutron star spins, the beam spins, too, like the beam of a searchlight. If we happen to lie along the pattern swept out by the beam, we see periodic flashes of light. Astronomers usually find neutron stars by the flashes of radiation that we see. The first ones were discovered in 1967. Since the radiation appears to pulse, or flash on and off, astronomers call them pulsars. Since we usually do not lie along the beam's path from a spinning neutron star, we find only a fraction of all neutron stars that exist. So far, astronomers have found about 2,000 pulsars, but the actual number must be far larger.

There is a second way to find neutron stars. Sometimes a neutron star is in a binary system with a normal star. If the two orbit very closely, the strong gravity of the neutron star can pull matter off the normal star and onto itself. However, the matter does not fall directly upon the neutron star. Rather, it forms a disk around the neutron star, and then matter slowly falls from the disk onto the neutron star. The plunge toward the disk and neutron star heats the gas to millions of degrees. This temperature is so high that the gas gives off X-rays. The earth's atmosphere blocks X-rays, so astronomers can observe X-ray sources only from above the earth's atmosphere. Astronomers discovered the first X-ray binary, Scorpius X-1, in 1961. Normal stars do not have enough gravity to produce the amount of X-rays that we see in X-ray binaries. Therefore, when we see an X-ray binary, we are not looking at two normal stars. That is, the unusual object that produces the X-rays must be much smaller and denser than a normal star. One possibility is a neutron star.

What is the other possibility? A black hole has even more gravity than a neutron star, so it could be in an X-ray binary. What is a black hole? A black hole is a star that is so massive and small that its gravity is very strong, even stronger than a neutron star. If you throw a ball into the air, it slows and then falls back to earth. You know that gravity is responsible for this. If we launch a rocket fast enough, it can escape the earth's gravity. To do that requires a speed of 25,000 mi/hr (40,000 km/hr), or about seven miles per second. If the earth's gravity were stronger, it would require a much higher speed to escape the earth. Light travels very quickly, 186,000 miles/s (300,000 km/s). A black hole's gravity is so strong that not even light can escape it. Since nothing can travel as fast as light, nothing that falls into a black hole can come back out, so it is a hole. Furthermore, since not even light cannot escape a black hole, a black hole would appear dark (or black).

Artist concept of a black hole.

You may ask, "Since black holes give off no light, how do we know that they exist?" While we may not directly see a black hole, we can see the effect that its gravity has on nearby matter. For instance, if a black hole is in a close binary system with a normal star, its intense gravity can pull matter off its companion, as a neutron star can. How can we tell if the compact object in an X-ray binary is a neutron star or a black hole? Remember that binary stars allow us to "weigh" stars to determine their masses. There is an upper limit of how much mass a neutron star can have, about two to three times the mass of the sun. Remember that we can measure the masses of stars in binary systems, so we can determine the mass of the compact object within an X-ray binary. The mass of the compact object in Scorpius X-1 is 1.4 times the mass of the sun. This is the minimum mass for a neutron star, so the compact object in Scorpius X-1 is a neutron star. On the other hand, the mass of the compact object in Cygnus X-1 is about 15 times the mass of the sun, so it must be a black hole. By the way, astronomers discovered Cygnus X-1 in 1964. It was the first black hole discovered. However, in the case of both Scorpius X-1 and Cygnus X-1, it took astronomers a few years to figure out what they were looking at.

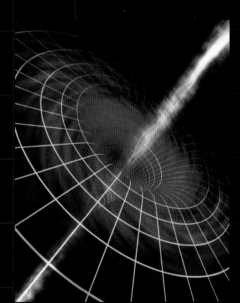

From time to time, a star erupts and becomes much brighter than it was before. The ancients called these new stars. The Latin word for new is *nova*, and this what we call these stars today. A nova does not stay at its new brightness for long. Soon it fades back to pretty much what it was before, so a nova is temporary. Usually, astronomers don't even notice the star before it becomes a nova.

What is a nova? We think that a nova happens in a close binary star where one of the stars is a white dwarf and the other star is a little larger than a main sequence star. The gravity of the white dwarf pulls matter off the companion star so that the matter transfers to the white dwarf from its companion. As

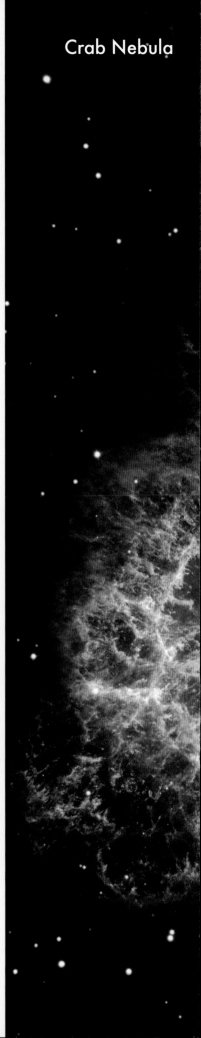

in an X-ray binary, the transferring matter doesn't fall directly onto the white dwarf but usually falls onto a disk around the white dwarf first. Most of the infalling material is hydrogen, something that the white dwarf does not have. As the hydrogen builds up on the surface of the white dwarf, the hydrogen heats. The strong gravity of the white dwarf compresses the hydrogen. Eventually, the pressure and temperature of the hydrogen increases until some of the hydrogen begins to fuse into helium, releasing more heat. This heat causes more fusion, which releases more heat, and very quickly the surface of the white dwarf erupts with energy. This is the rapid increase in brightness that we notice as a nova. Eventually, all the hydrogen is used up, and things settle down. Matter once again begins to fall from the other star onto the white dwarf, and the process repeats. The length of time between each eruption can be thousands of years, so we're not likely to see the same star do this twice.

Nearly a century ago, astronomers realized that there are other stars that blow up far more than a novae does (novae is plural for nova). Since these stars are far brighter, astronomers call them supernovae. What are supernovae? Astronomers recognize two basic types of supernovae, types I and II, but there are several subtypes, such as type Ia, type Ib, and type Ic. Astronomers think that the different types of supernovae go through different processes. We think that type Ia supernovae happen in close binary stars similar to the systems that produce novae. There is maximum mass that a white dwarf star may have, about 1.4 times the mass of the sun. If the white dwarf in the binary system gains enough mass to reach this limit, the white dwarf explodes, totally destroying the star. The energy given off is the brightening of the supernova.

Other types of supernovae probably come from very massive single stars. Astronomers think that some of these stars have exhausted all sources of fuel in their cores. Unable to produce more energy, their cores collapse. This collapse takes place very rapidly, releasing a tremendous amount of energy. That energy tears through the outer layers of the star, heating the gas in the outer layers and causing it to fly away into space. Eventually much of the energy is released and the supernova fades, but years later we can see the expanding envelope of gas as a supernova remnant. One of the most famous supernova remnants is the Crab Nebula in the constellation Taurus. Its location matches that of a supernova that Chinese astronomers saw in the year A.D. 1054. Astronomers have measured the rate at which the Crab Nebula is expanding. From its rate of expansion, astronomers have determined that the expansion must have started about the year A.D. 1054.

If the core of the massive star collapses, what is left behind? We think that it leaves behind either a neutron star or a black hole. Which kind of object is left depends upon how much mass it has. Recall that there is maximum mass that a neutron star can have. If the object left behind is too massive to be a neutron star, then it is a black hole. The Crab Nebula has a pulsar, a rapidly spinning neutron star at its center. This greatly supports the theory of what supernovae are.

Extrasolar Planets

MISSION LOG

EXTRASOLAR
EXOPLANET
MAIN SEQUENCE STAR
TRANSIT
HABITABLE ZONE

Perhaps a majority of stars in the solar neighborhood are members of binary star systems, for binaries appear to be common. The sun is a bit odd in this respect, because it does not have a stellar companion. However, the sun does have its planets orbiting it. For many years, astronomers thought that other stars might host planets as well, but that was speculation. This all changed in the 1990s as technology finally allowed astronomers to discover planets orbiting other stars. We call planets orbiting other stars *extrasolar* planets, meaning planets outside of the sun, or solar system. We shall discuss just a few of the more common ways that astronomers find extrasolar planets.

Astronomers had failed to detect extrasolar planets previously, because any planets so close to their stars would be much too faint to be easily visible. Imagine that we were to look at the solar system from the distance of even the nearest stars. Planets shine only because of the light that they reflect from the sun. At the distance of the nearest stars, most of the sun's planets, including the earth, would be far too faint for even the largest telescopes now in use to be visible. Jupiter, the brightest planet, would be barely bright enough to see, but it would be about 20 magnitudes (100 million times) fainter than the sun. It would appear very close to the sun, and the glare of the sun would obscure Jupiter. Even with these difficulties, astronomers have found a few extrasolar planets this way, starting in 2004.

THE STARS OF HEAVEN

I Chronicles 16:31

*Let the heavens rejoice,
and let the earth be glad;
And let them say among the nations,
"The Lord reigns."*

The first was 2M1207b, a planet orbiting the faint star 2M1207. Astronomers name extrasolar planets by adding a lowercase letter to the name of the parent star. They start with the letter b for the first planet found and go through the alphabet if they find additional planets. More famous are the planets Fomalhaut b (discovered in 2008) and Beta Pictoris b. Beta Pictoris b was discovered in 2003, but that discovery remained controversial for several years. This method even yielded a system of three planets around the star HR 8799 (HR 8799b, HR 8799c, and HR 8799d). The method of direct imaging probably will improve tremendously with a new telescope especially designed to do this difficult work.

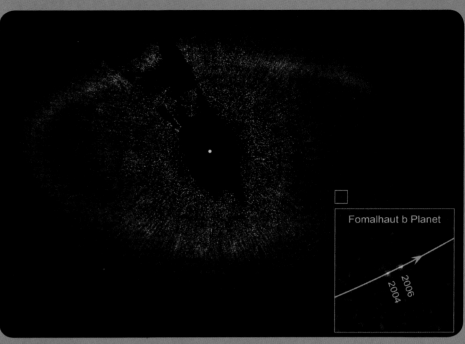

Fomalhaut b Planet

2006
2004

This image shows Fomalhaut, the star around which the newly discovered planet orbits. Fomalhaut is much hotter than our sun, 15 times as bright, and lies 25 light-years from Earth.

A much easier method is to look for motion in a star as its planet orbits it. As we saw with binary stars, both stars move as they orbit. How much they move depends upon their masses: the more mass that a star has, the less that it moves. Stars have far more mass than their planets, so they move very little compared to their planets, but they do move. In most cases, we would expect that a star would alternately move toward us and then away from us each orbit that its planet makes. This will show up as a Doppler motion shifting back and forth each orbit. The evidence of this sort of motion is very feeble, and the technology to measure it did not exist until the 1990s. The first extrasolar planet discovered orbiting a main sequence star, 51 Pegasi b, was found with this method in 1995. The Doppler method has been one of the most successful methods of finding extrasolar planets.

Another successful method for finding extrasolar planets is by transit. A transit is when a smaller body passes in front of a larger body. A transit is a type of eclipse, but because the eclipsing body is so small, it blocks out only a small portion of the larger body's light. Imagine that we were to view the sun from a location far away but in the plane of the earth's orbit. Once each orbit (one year), the earth would transit the sun. The transit would take about 13.5 hours. The sun is about 100 times the diameter of the earth. This means that the surface area of the sun visible from our distant vantage point would be about 10,000 times greater than the earth's surface area. This would cause a decrease in the sun's brightness by 0.01 percent for about 13.5 hours. This is not much of a decrease, but we have instruments on some telescopes that can do this. The largest planet, Jupiter, would block out about 1 percent of the sun's light. We would expect that similar things would be visible in the light of other stars as any planets that they might have orbiting them.

Star

Planet

Brightness

Light Curve

Time

Astronomers have found several extrasolar planets using the transit method with telescopes on earth. However, the Kepler spacecraft found hundreds, and possibly thousands, of extrasolar planets. Launched in 2009, Kepler's mission lasted until 2013. During its mission, Kepler continually measured more than 150,000 stars to an accuracy of 0.001 percent. This is adequate to detect virtually all of the sun's planets, if we were viewing the sun from near the plane of the planets' orbits and if their orbital periods were short enough for transits to have happened. We generally are not in the orbital plane of any particular extrasolar planet, so this method will miss many potential planets orbiting other stars. Furthermore, if an extrasolar planet orbits far from its star, we were not likely to observe a transit in the little more than three years of the Kepler mission. For instance, the orbital period of Jupiter is 12 years, so the Kepler would have had about a one in four chance of detecting it, assuming that we were viewing the sun from the plane of Jupiter's orbit.

The Kepler mission discovered more than 1,000 extrasolar planets. We are unlikely to detect the vast majority of extrasolar planets, so the fact that we have found so many suggests that extrasolar planets are very common. Why are scientists so interested in extrasolar planets? Most scientists believe in evolution, that life on earth arose naturally, and that humans are simply evolved animals. That is, they do not believe in creation, as taught in the Bible. But if this is the only planet on which there is life, then that would suggest that life is very special, so special as to require a Creator. Therefore, many scientists think that there must be many inhabited planets. The first step in establishing this is to show that planets like the earth are common. Since we know that right now we are capable of finding only a small fraction of all extrasolar planets, the total number of planets must be huge.

Launch of the Delta II rocket with Kepler spacecraft (2009).

What have the extrasolar planets thus far discovered told us? First, we have not found any earth-like planets. Astronomers define the habitable zone around a star. Liquid water appears to be essential for life, but many planets are either too hot or too cold for liquid water to exist. This happens if a planet's orbit is too close or too far from the star. There is a narrow range around any star where liquid water could exist. Of course, the earth is in the middle of the sun's habitable zone, but Venus is too close to the sun, and Mars is too far. However, orbital distance from the star alone is not enough. The moon is the proper distance from the sun, but it is lifeless. The reason is that the moon has no atmosphere to provide enough pressure and warmth for liquid water. To have a sufficient atmosphere, a planet must have the proper mass and size so that the surface gravity can retain an atmosphere. On the other hand, if a planet is too massive, like the Jovian planets, its atmosphere is made of the wrong gases. Even if a planet is in the habitable zone and has the right size, the stars themselves are wrong. Some stars produce much radiation that is harmful to life. Many stars similar to the sun are variable and likely produce strong magnetic storms that are harmful for life. While there are more than a thousand confirmed extrasolar planets, none is like the earth.

The discovery of extrasolar planets has given evolutionists other problems. Not only do evolutionists have theories about how life supposedly arose on earth, they have evolutionary theories about how planets formed. This theory requires that small planets form near their stars and that large planets form far from their stars. Of course, this is to model what our solar system is like. However, many extrasolar planets are very large but also very close to their stars. Many of these huge planets orbit far closer to their stars than Mercury orbits the sun. According to the theory of how planets naturally formed, most of these planets ought not to exist. They could rewrite the theories to explain how these planetary systems formed, but then that would not explain our solar system. At the very least, it seems that our solar system is unusual, with small planets close to the sun and large planets far from the sun. Perhaps this ought to tell us that our solar system, along with the earth, is unique in creation. That is hard to explain if the world has evolved, but not if God created the world.

Astronomers discovered the first extrasolar planets in 1992. That year, astronomers discovered two planets orbiting the pulsar PSR B1257+12, and a third soon followed. The problem is that planets ought not to be orbiting a pulsar. Pulsars supposedly form from a supernova explosion in a star. That explosion ought to destroy any planets that may have orbited the star, so it is difficult to explain naturally how they might form after a supernova.

There's No Place Like Earth! From time to time, you will see news reports of new planets being discovered that scientist theorize could support life like that on Earth on planets that would either be like Earth or support alternate forms of life. NASA currently uses the Kepler Space Telescope to find planets that are orbiting stars in a habitable zone in trying to discover other places that may support life within the known universe.

Remember, it is only within the last 20 years that the existence of extrasolar, also known as exoplanets, have been known.

Trying to prove everything from evolutionary theories to the existence of alien worlds, these theories center around trying to counteract a powerful truth — if Earth and its life is unique — in a universe of countless planets and stars without life, it implies a Creator rather than a lottery-style game of chance that by the sheer number of celestial bodies should have happened numerous times in one way or another.

"Hopes of finding life within our own solar system have been dashed so far, but that has not diminished the astronomical zeal. In 2009 NASA launched the Kepler telescope — costing over half a billion dollars — to monitor 145,000 stars for evidence of orbiting planets. The results are astounding: over 3,500 candidates were identified in Kepler's small survey. Yet Kepler was able to detect just a small fraction of the planets orbiting its target stars. Correcting for its limited view and extending the result to other stars, researchers can estimate how many planets exist. Our Milky Way galaxy alone may host as many as 100 billion planets. Despite the hype, the survey is verifying what our solar system has already shown us — that there's no place like home."[11]

CHAPTER 10

Star Clusters & Nebulae

> **Level 1**
> **Level 2**
> **Level 3**

MISSION LOG

STAR CLUSTERS
OPEN CLUSTERS
GLOBULAR CLUSTERS
INTERSTELLAR MEDIUM
SILICATE
NEBULA
DARK NEBULA
REFLECTION NEBULA
MOLECULAR CLOUDS

As we have seen, many stars are members of binary systems. Both binary stars and single stars are distributed in space. Astronomers call these "field stars." However, with telescopes we see in space that there are many clumps of stars. These clumps are star clusters. The stars in a cluster are packed together much more closely than field stars are.

They are close enough that most clusters are bound together by their mutual gravity. That is, the stars in a cluster orbit around a common center of mass. The Pleiades, sometimes called the Seven Sisters, is the brightest and best-known cluster. It looks like a very small dipper above and to the right of the constellation Orion. In fact, when people notice the Pleiades, many of them mistakenly think that the Pleiades star cluster is the Little Dipper.

The Pleiades are mentioned three times in the Old Testament (Job 9:9, 38:31–32, and Amos 5:8). Each time they are mentioned in conjunction with Orion, probably because of their close proximity in the sky. Job 38:31 asks, "Can you bind the chains of the Pleiades or loose the cords of Orion?" (ESV). We are not sure what that means. Some people think that the chains of the Pleiades might refer to the gravity holding the cluster together.

There are two types of star clusters — open clusters and globular clusters. The Pleiades is an example of an open cluster. Open clusters typically have a few dozen to a few thousand stars. Open clusters have an irregular appearance. Globular clusters have far more stars, anywhere from 50,000 to a million stars. Rather than having an irregular shape, globular clusters are spherical. That is why we call them globular clusters, coming from the word globe. Compare the photographs of the open and globular clusters. If you turn the book upside-down, the open cluster will look different, but the globular cluster will look about the same. There are

THE STARS OF HEAVEN

Amos 5:8

He made the Pleiades and Orion
He turns the shadow of death
into morning...

other differences between open clusters and globular clusters, such as the types of stars that they contain, and where they are located in the galaxy.

The space between the stars is very empty. If there was much matter between the stars, that matter would obscure the stars. For a long time astronomers thought that the space between the stars was absolutely empty. However, nearly a century ago astronomers began to understand that there was a little bit of matter between the stars. Astronomers call this stuff between the stars the interstellar medium. Over the years, astronomers have learned much about the interstellar medium. The interstellar medium is very thin. In most places, the interstellar medium is much thinner than the best vacuum that we can produce on earth. Much of the matter in the interstellar medium is in the form of gas. Much of this is in the form of atoms, but there are some molecules present. There are microscopic solid particles in the interstellar medium as well. We call these particles *dust*. Many of the dust particles are rod-shaped. The dust particles are made of iron, silicate (a kind of rock), and ice.

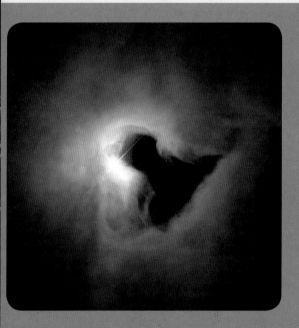

The interstellar medium is very clumpy. This means that some regions are much thinner than average, while other regions are much thicker than average. Astronomers call the thick regions of the interstellar medium clouds. Another word for them is *nebula*, the Latin word for cloud. The plural form is nebulae. Dust particles block starlight as it passes through. This makes stars appear fainter and redder than they normally do. Astronomers must account for this in much of their work. Sometimes the dust is so thick that they form clouds that completely obscure stars beyond them. Through a telescope, it appears as if there is a hole in the sky where there are no stars. We call this a *dark nebula*. Sometimes the light of hot, bright stars near the nebula scatters, or reflects off the dust. We call this a *reflection nebula* (left). A reflection nebula appears blue in color photographs.

If a large cloud of hydrogen gas is around very hot, bright stars, the ultraviolet light of the stars ionizes the hydrogen gas. Ionization is the removal of electrons from atoms. The electrical current in a fluorescent light ionizes the mercury gas inside. As electrons recombine with atoms, they give off visible light. This is how a fluorescent light works, but the same process also causes the hydrogen gas around the hot stars to glow. Astronomers call these glowing clouds *HII regions*. In color photographs, HII regions appear red, but if you look at one through a telescope, it probably will look white. This is because the color-sensitive cells in our eyes require a lot of light. However, our black and white sensitive cells record the red light as white. One of the best examples of an HII region is the Orion Nebula, located in the center star marking Orion's sword.

There are clouds of hydrogen gas far from any hot, bright stars. These clouds are very cold. Astronomers call these cold clouds of hydrogen *HI regions*. HI regions do not give off visible light, but they do emit radiation in the radio part of the spectrum. Astronomers use this radio emission to map the locations of HI regions in our galaxy.

The largest and densest regions of the interstellar medium are *molecular clouds* (right). We call them this because they contain molecules, as well as atoms and dust particles. Many astronomers think that stars are born in molecular clouds. The Bible tells us that God made the stars on the fourth day a few thousand years ago, but many astronomers do not believe this. Instead, they think that the universe began 13.8 billion years ago in a big bang. We learned earlier that the sun gets its energy from the fusion of hydrogen into helium. Most stars probably get their energy the same way. This source of energy cannot work forever, because the hydrogen fuel eventually will

run out. For the sun, we estimate that the fuel could last for at most ten billion years. Since this is less than 13.8 billion years, astronomers think that the sun did not exist for much of the history of the universe. Many other stars have lifetimes far less than the sun has, so astronomers reason that those stars must have formed long after the beginning of the universe. In other words, evolutionary astronomers must have stars forming throughout billions of years and continuing today. Of course, if the universe is only thousands of years old as the Bible indicates, then stars need not form at all today.

From time to time, there are news reports of astronomers witnessing the birth of a star. This is not true. Theoretically, the process of star birth is very slow, far too slow for someone to see a new star where none was there before. Instead, astronomers find what appear to be stars in the later stages of what astronomers think is the process that a cloud must go through as it transforms into a star. This amounts to arranging snapshots into a story. Some creation scientists think that since God created stars on day 4, and then ceased creating after day 6, that He is not making stars anymore. Other creation scientists think that as some stars "die" God ordained some physical processes that occasionally would allow more stars to form.

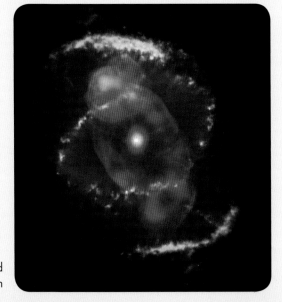

Cat's Eye Nebula, a planetary nebula believed to be formed by the death of a star with about the same mass as the sun

Globular Cluster

63

Our Galaxy: The Milky Way

> Level 1
> Level 2
> Level 3

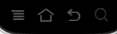

MISSION LOG

SPIRAL TRACERS
NEBULAE
SPIRAL NEBULAE
CEPHEID VARIABLES
SPIRAL GALAXIES
IRREGULAR GALAXIES
LOCAL GROUP
DWARF GALAXIES

If you go outside on a dark, clear night in late summer or early autumn, you will see a streak of light crossing the entire sky. That is the Milky Way. Alternately, we call it the *galaxy*, from a Greek word that means milk. Before the invention of the telescope, people did not know what the Milky Way was. Four centuries ago, Galileo recorded what he saw along the Milky Way with his telescope. He saw many thousands of stars too faint to see with the eye alone. He quickly realized that the faint light of these many stars blended to give that milky appearance. Soon people figured out that stars were not randomly or uniformly distributed in space. Rather, the stars are arranged in a flat disk. More than two hundred years ago, a famous astronomer named William Herschel determined that the sun was near the center of the galaxy. That belief remained until about a century ago. We now think that we are about halfway from the galaxy center.

The Milky Way galaxy is much too large for us to send spacecraft out to take photographs of it from the outside. And our view from inside is obscured some by dust in the galaxy. Still, astronomers have managed to probe the galaxy's structure, and we can compare it to other galaxies to get an idea of what the Milky Way galaxy looks like. The galaxy is round and flat, with a bulge at its center. The diameter of the disk is about 100,000 light years. Much of the disk is about a thousand light years thick, but the bulge is considerably thicker, nearly 10,000 light years. There is a bar running across the galactic bulge. Two spiral-shaped arms come off the ends of the bar. The sun is located near one of the spiral arms.

THE STARS OF HEAVEN

Hebrews 1:10

*And, Thou, Lord, in the beginning ha
laid the foundation of the earth; and t
heavens are the works of thine hand.*

What are the spiral arms? Because the arms are so bright, it is easy to get the impression that most of the stars are along the spiral arms. However, this is not correct. The density of stars between the spiral arms is about the same as it is along the spiral arms. The difference is that the hottest and brightest stars, the O, B, and A spectral types, are along the spiral arms. This makes the spiral arms appear so bright. Astronomers call O and B type stars spiral tracers. This is because O and B stars are so easy to see, and they trace out the locations of the spiral arms. Other spiral tracers include HI and HII regions, as well as dark nebulae and molecular clouds. We can clearly see spiral arms in other galaxies, and studies of those galaxies help us to understand the spiral arms in our own galaxy.

Spiral arms present a problem for people who believe that the universe is many billions of years old. The matter in each galaxy appears to be orbiting around the galaxy's center of mass. But matter near the center ought to orbit more quickly than matter farther away from the center. After a few rotations, the spiral arms would smear so that they disappear. For instance, we estimate that the sun and stars around it would take about 250 million years to orbit the galaxy once. If the galaxy is at least 12 billion years old, as most astronomers think, then the portion of the galaxy in the sun's vicinity would have orbited nearly 50 times. The spiral arms would have smeared out long ago, so why do the Milky Way and similar galaxies still have spiral arms? Since the 1960s, astronomers have suggested at least three different mechanisms that could maintain spiral arms for billions of years. The fact that astronomers keep inventing new theories of how this might work indicates that the mechanisms really don't work. Of course, if the universe is only thousands of years old, this isn't a problem.

Surrounding the disk of the galaxy is the halo. Unlike the disk, the halo is spherical. The diameter of the halo is about the same as the disk diameter, about 100,000 light years. The halo contains far fewer stars than the disk, and very little gas and dust. The stars in the halo tend to be fainter and redder than disk stars. But the very grand globular star clusters are in the halo. The open star clusters are in the disk of the galaxy.

Other Galaxies Once astronomers began to understand the structure of the Milky Way galaxy, some began to wonder if there were other galaxies. With the naked eye, you can see a few fuzzy objects in the sky. Stars appear as pinpoints, but these objects appeared slightly larger. Since these objects appeared cloudy, ancient astronomers called these fuzzy objects *nebulae*, meaning cloudy. With the invention of the telescope, astronomers began to find many more nebulae too faint for the eye alone to see. Some of these nebulae turned out to be star clusters. It took telescopes to reveal their individual stars. But other nebulae remained fuzzy, suggesting that they were clouds of glowing gas within our galaxy. Some of the nebulae appeared round and flat, with bulges at their centers. Eventually, astronomers saw arms spiraling out from the centers of some, so astronomers called these *spiral nebulae* (right). Astronomers wondered if the spiral nebulae might be very distant galaxies outside of our Milky Way, but similar in structure.

However, by 1800 another theory of what these spiral nebulae were came about. Astronomers think that stars form from gas clouds, which is not a new idea. More than two centuries ago, some astronomers suggested that the spiral nebulae were new solar systems in development. The bulge at the center was the condensation of most of the gas from which the new star would eventually form. The disk was the leftover material from the star's formation. The spiral arms were pieces of the disk that eventually would form into planets. Astronomers debated these two theories about the spiral nebulae for much of the 19th century. However, by 1880, the idea that these were solar systems in the making became the dominant theory, and it remained so until 1924. A century ago many astronomers used photographs of spiral nebulae to prove that their evolutionary ideas of how stars and solar systems formed were true. This ought to cause us to be very doubtful about the many announcements today of new stars being born.

In 1924, astronomers abruptly abandoned the idea that the spiral nebulae were developing solar systems in favor of the spiral nebulae being distant galaxies. What caused them to change their minds? That year, Edwin Hubble, using what was then the largest telescope in the world, the 100-inch telescope on Mt. Wilson in southern California, managed to photograph individual stars in M31. M31 is the largest and brightest-appearing of the spiral nebulae. Whatever the spiral nebulae were, M31's brightness and large size suggested that it was the closest spiral nebula. The stars that Hubble was able to photograph were very faint. They were so faint that it stretched the limits of what even the 100-inch telescope could do at the time.

Spiral Galaxy
NGC 1300

Hubble recognized that some of the stars that he had found were Cepheid variables. Cepheid variables have unique characteristics that make them easy to identify, so Hubble was confident of his discovery. More importantly, Cepheid variables are giant and supergiant stars, making them some of the brightest stars. The fact that the Cepheid variables in M31 were so faint meant that they and M31 had to be very far away, far outside of our galaxy. Hubble was even able to use Cepheid variables to estimate the distance to M31. Today we think that M31 is a little more than two million light years away. It is the closest galaxy similar in size to the Milky Way galaxy. A more common name for M31 is the Andromeda Galaxy, so called, because it is in the constellation Andromeda. You can see it on a very dark, clear night in autumn, if you know where to look.

We have been calling M31 and similar galaxies *spiral nebulae.* That is what astronomers back in Hubble's time called them, because astronomers thought that the galaxies were nebulae, or clouds of gas, within our Milky Way galaxy. The term spiral nebulae was used for a while after Hubble, but it is an outdated term. Today it is proper to call them *spiral galaxies.*

Once Hubble showed that there were many other galaxies, he set out to study galaxies themselves. The first step was to classify galaxies. We have already seen one type, the spiral galaxies. But there are two types of spiral galaxies: *normal spirals* and *barred spirals.* Normal spiral galaxies have spiral arms that come off the bulges in their centers. Barred spirals have bars passing through their central bulges, and their spiral arms come off of the ends of their bars.

For a long time, astronomers thought that the Milky Way was a normal spiral, but now they are pretty certain that the Milky Way is a barred spiral. It is difficult to tell, because we are inside the galaxy instead of outside looking in. Furthermore, we are far from the center (about 25,000 light years), and the dust between us and the center blocks much of the light from the center. Hubble designated normal spirals with a capital letter S, and he used the letters SB to indicate barred spirals. Hubble also had subclasses of spiral galaxies, depending upon how tightly the spiral arms were wound and the size of the nucleus, or bulge, in each galaxy. Hubble called spiral galaxies with large nuclei and tight arms Sa. He called spiral galaxies with smaller nuclei and more loose arms Sb, and he called the spiral galaxies with the smallest nuclei and the loosest arms, Sc. He had similar designations for the barred spirals, SBa, SBb, and SBc.

Spiral Galaxy
Messier 83

Other galaxies don't have disks or spiral arms. Instead, they have an elliptical shape. An ellipse can be round, but an ellipse may appear flattened, sort of like an oval. Hubble called these galaxies *ellipticals*, indicated by a capital letter E. He had subclasses depending upon how flattened the galaxies appeared. The round galaxies were E0, slightly flattened were E1, and so forth up to E7 for the flattest galaxies. Hubble could not fit some galaxies into either group. These he called *irregular galaxies*, indicated by the abbreviation Irr. About, 1 to 2 percent of galaxies are irregular.

For years, many astronomers thought that galaxies evolved from one type to the other. Some thought that elliptical galaxies evolved into spiral galaxies, while others thought that spiral galaxies evolved into ellipticals. Eventually, astronomers concluded that

galaxies usually don't evolve from one type to another. Now astronomers think that clliptical galaxies start out that way, and that spiral galaxies start out that way. The only way that astronomers now think that a galaxy may change from one type to another is when two spiral galaxies collide and merge into one galaxy. Theoretically, this results in a larger elliptical galaxy. The largest galaxies are the giant ellipticals, and astronomers think that they might have formed from the mergers of many galaxies. These changing ideas illustrate how much man's ideas about the world change. We cannot be certain about what science tells us, particular when science supposedly tells us about how our world and we got here. But we can be sure that God does not change, and so we can be certain that what He tells us in His Word, the Bible, does not change and is true.

Two Interacting Spiral Galaxies

Another example of change in the thinking about galaxies is the way that astronomers think galaxies form. For many years, astronomers thought that very large clouds of gas condensed to form galaxies. Astronomers thought that as the clouds condensed to form galaxies, the gas formed into stars within the galaxies as well. We call this the top-down theory, because it starts with structures on the size of galaxies that form stars. Now most astronomers believe in a bottom-up theory, that stars formed first and then joined together to form galaxies.

Galaxy Cluster

Dwarf Galaxy

As we tend to find stars grouped together into clusters within galaxies, galaxies tend to group together, too. We call these groups of galaxies *galaxy clusters*. The nearest galaxy cluster is the Virgo Cluster, so called because it is in the direction of the constellation Virgo. The Virgo cluster contains about a thousand galaxies. The distance to the Virgo Cluster is 40 to 50 million light years. The Milky Way is a bit odd in that it is not a member of a galaxy cluster. Instead, the Milky Way is a member of a modest collection of galaxies that we call the *Local Group*. The local group contains two large spiral galaxies, M31 and the Milky Way. The local group also contains another spiral galaxy, M33, that is a little smaller than the other two. The rest of the Local Group is several score of very small galaxies. Astronomers call such small galaxies *dwarf galaxies*. Many of them orbit around a much larger galaxy as satellites. M31 has two satellite galaxies that show up in most photographs of M31. The Milky Way has two satellites galaxies, the Large Magellanic Cloud and the Small Magellanic Cloud. The Local Group may be a sort of satellite of the Virgo Cluster.

In the 1930s, an astronomer named Fritz Zwicky studied clusters of galaxies. From the motions of the galaxies within clusters, it appeared that galaxy clusters contained far more mass than could be explained by the galaxies themselves. Often galaxy clusters contained ten times more mass than the galaxies appeared to have. Beginning in the 1970s, astronomers studying the rotations of spiral galaxies found a similar thing. The rotations of these galaxies showed that there was much mass beyond where nearly all the light from the galaxy was coming. The problem is, this mass doesn't give off any light. Astronomers now call this dark matter. What is dark matter? No one knows. How much dark matter is there? Estimates vary, but it appears that there is far more dark matter than matter that we can see.

Evolutionists have used dark matter to solve various problems in their theories. This has led some creationists to think that dark matter does not exist. That is, some creationists seem to think that dark matter was invented solely to save evolutionary ideas. However, there is good evidence for dark matter. The fact that once evolutionists realized that dark matter probably exists and so they use it in their theories ought to have nothing to do with the question of whether dark matter exists. Other creationists are excited by the possibility that we don't know what most of the universe is made of. There doesn't appear to be a place for any new type of matter in our theory of physics. If dark matter is real, it probably will require a revision of physics. It is humbling that our Creator has created so many mysteries for us.

How do creationists view galaxies? We think that God made them on day 4 of the creation week, pretty much as we see them today. It is interesting that astronomers now think that they have found galaxies about 12 billion light years away. This distance suggests that we see these galaxies as they appeared 12 billion years ago. Since astronomers think that the universe is just 13.8 billion years old, these galaxies must be very young. Yet, these galaxies look almost exactly like nearby galaxies. This is consistent with what we think about creation, that God made the galaxies pretty much as galaxies appear today.

We Live in the Milky Way Though ancient civilizations assumed that Earth was the center of the universe, and that the whole universe was what we now call The Milky Way, we have learned over thousands of years that we are not the center of the universe. We are part of one galaxy in a universe filled with countless other galaxies. We are not even at the center of the Milky Way, but instead are part of just one of many spiral arms of the galaxy. Here are some cool facts about our galaxy:

- Contains an estimated 100 billion stars and up to 400 billion planets[12]
- The farther from the center of the galaxy, the number of starts decrease
- Has a huge galactic halo of stars and globular clusters that surround it[13]
- Our solar system is located within the Orion spiral arm of the galaxy[14]
- A black hole is purported to be at the center of this galaxy.[15]

Barred Spiral Galaxy NGC_6217

12

Light - Travel - Time Problem

> **Level 1**
> **Level 2**
> **Level 3**

MISSION LOG

GENERAL RELATIVITY
WHITE HOLE THEORY
DIMENSION
ASC SOLUTION
DASHA
EX NIHILO

Exodus 20:11 tells us that God created the world (including the astronomical world) in six days. Furthermore, the chronologies found in the Old Testament indicate that the creation week was about 6,000 years ago. You may wonder how we can see any galaxies if they are millions or billions of light years away. Even many stars within our galaxy are farther than 6,000 light years away, so how can we see them? Indeed, this is a problem for the recent creation model. We even have a name for this, the light-travel-time problem. Creation scientists have offered several explanations for this problem.

However, before explaining some of those proposed solutions, perhaps we ought to describe more carefully the problem. By concentrating on what we can see today, 6,000 years after creation, we sort of assume that people could always have seen the nearest stars. But what did Adam see at the end of the creation week? As the darkness fell upon Adam and Eve for the first time, they must have seen stars, or else the stars could not have filled their functions given in Genesis 1:14–19. However, the nearest star is more than four light years away. Most stars that we see at night are dozens, or even hundreds, of light years away. How could Adam have seen them? To truly solve the light-travel-time problem, we must explain how Adam and Eve saw stars right away. Once we explain that, we probably can explain the light-travel-time problem today.

What are some of the solutions to the light-travel-time problem? Many creationists think that God made the world mature. That is, Adam and Eve weren't babies, but began their lives as adults. Similarly, God made mature plants, or else the animals and Adam and Eve would not have had anything to eat. In short, God probably made the entire universe fully functioning and mature. In similar manner, perhaps God made the light already on its way to the earth so that the stars are mature. This has been a popular solution to the light-travel-time problem, and remains so today. But many people realize that this solution would mean that light that we are now receiving from most

THE STARS OF HEAVEN

Exodus 20:11

For in six days the Lord made the heavens and the earth, the sea, and all that is in them, and rested the seventh day.

of the objects in the universe never actually left those objects. Thus, much of the universe would amount to a sort of mirage or image. Many find this unsettling, so they have searched for other solutions.

Another solution to the light-travel-time problem is the suggestion that the speed of light was much higher in the past. If the speed of light were much greater, perhaps infinite, in the early universe, then light could easily have reached the earth from the most distant parts of the universe. While supporters of this idea have offered evidence for a decreasing speed of light, many creation scientists don't agree that the evidence shows a decrease in light speed. Furthermore, the speed of light depends upon two fundamental constants of nature that determine the strength of electrical and magnetic forces. If the speed of light were to change, these other forces would change, and that would change the structure of matter.

Artist's View of a Black Hole in a Globular Cluster

Another proposed solution to the light-travel-time problem is based upon Albert Einstein's theory of general relativity. General relativity is our current theory of gravity, and it relates space and time to matter and energy. One peculiarity of general relativity is that time does not pass at the same rate everywhere. Rather, the rate, or speed, with which time passes depends upon one's location and the amount of matter and energy present. The creation physicist Russ Humphreys has suggested that God created a white hole on day 1 of the creation week. A white hole is like a black hole running in reverse. Instead of matter and energy falling into the hole, matter and energy fly outward from the hole. As matter and energy exit a white hole, it would get smaller and eventually go away. However, time would pass at very different rates inside and outside the white hole. If the earth is inside the white hole and stars are outside, millions of years might pass for the stars and the space outside but only a few days on the earth. By the end of the creation week, the white hole disappeared, and since then time has passed at about the same rate for most of the universe. But the great time that occurred on day 4 when God made the stars would allow the light from the most distant objects in the universe to reach the earth while only a day or two passed on earth. Inspired by these ideas, John Hartnett, another creation physicist, used an alternate theory of relativity to arrive at a slightly different solution to the light-travel-time problem. General relativity works with four dimensions — three dimensions of space and one dimension of time. However, Hartnett used a version that has a fifth dimension.

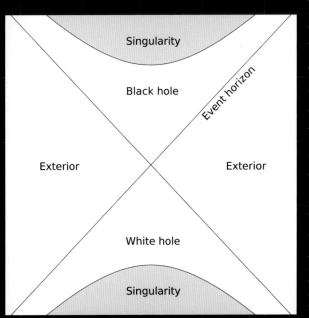

A creation astronomer, Jason Lisle, has suggested a very different solution to the light-travel-time problem. He calls it the anisotropic synchrony convention (ASC) solution. Our measurements of the speed of light rely upon a two-way trip for the light. Scientists send light to a mirror, and the mirror reflects the light back to where the light started. The scientists can measure the time that the total trip makes, and by dividing twice the distance between the light source and the mirror by the elapsed time, they find the speed of light. But this assumes that the light traveled both outward and back at the same speed. What if the light took no time to travel during one-half of its total journey, say from the light source to the mirror? Then the light would have to take the entire time to travel the other half of its journey back to the light source. The speed one way would then be infinite, and the speed the other way would be half what we think that the speed of light is. You see, all that we can measure is the average speed during the light's journey back and forth. What if light took no time at all to travel from the stars to the earth? Presumably, light traveling from the earth to the stars would go only half as fast as we think. But this also would mean that it would take no time at all for light to arrive on earth from the most distant objects in the universe. While this solution might be possible, it strikes many people as a bit contrived.

Illustration of Speed of Light

Finally, the author of this book has proposed what he calls the *dasha* solution to the light-travel-time problem. Many people think that God created everything during the creation week *ex nihilo*. *Ex nihilo* is Latin for "out of nothing," and it suggests instantaneous creation. The creation of the heavens and earth in Genesis 1:1 at the beginning of the creation week was *ex nihilo*, and it likely was instantaneous, but was this the method throughout the creation week? A careful reading of the creation week account in Genesis 1 and the details of man's creation in Genesis 2 show that it was not. God made man from the dust of the ground. Therefore, man wasn't made from nothing, and it appears that God might have taken a moment or two to form man. Genesis 1:11 records that on day 3 God commanded the earth to bring forth all sorts of plants, and Genesis 1:12 records that the earth brought forth all sorts of plants. The two verbs used here, *bring* forth and *brought* forth, in English are the same word in different tenses, but in the Hebrew (the Old Testament was written mostly in Hebrew), there are two different words used here. The two verbs have more or less the same meaning. One of these verbs is *dasha*. Some English translations of the Bible read that the earth produced or sprouted plants on day 3. Other possible meanings are that the plants thrust or shot upward. From these words, it appears that the plants did not just instantaneously appear on day 3. Rather, they rapidly grew out of the ground, sort of like a time-lapse movie. This was a process of normal growth, but rapidly sped up. Why did God rapidly grow the plants on day 3? They had a function of providing food for man and beast. Today, people and many animals eat plants, but many people and some animals also eat other animals. But Genesis 1:30 tells us that originally man and all animals ate only plants. Those plants had to be mature so that they could produce food for Adam, Eve, and all the animals to eat just two or three days after God made the plants. If the plants could not produce food, then they could not fulfill their function.

In a similar manner, God may have not made the sun, moon, stars, and other astronomical bodies *ex nihilo* on day 4. Rather, He may have made them out of matter that He had created *ex nihilo* on day 1. So instead of making astronomical bodies instantly, God may have formed them very rapidly, much as He formed plants on day 3 and Adam's body on day 6. However, if the light of the stars was not visible at least by the end of day 6, the stars could not fulfill their functions of providing light, ruling the night, and being for signs, marking the passage of time, and for keeping calendars. So God must have "matured" the light by causing it to bring forth, or sprout, much as He made the plants come forth the previous day. Many Old Testament passages speak of God stretching out the heavens. It appears that in some of those passages the stretching is in the past tense (e.g., Jeremiah 51:15). Could it be that this stretching refers to the stretching of light to arrive on earth by the end of day 4?

So creationists have offered several solutions to the light-travel-time problem. Some people let this problem bother them, but in worrying about this, they overlook something. Creating this marvelous and huge universe is a far greater thing than any of us can comprehend. If God is powerful enough to call the entire universe into existence, then getting the light to us on earth is a trivial matter by comparison. Perhaps those who worry about this problem don't quite grasp how tremendous the creation is.

What about time travel for something other than just light? Unlike ancient discoveries of planets and stars, more modern discoveries and a thriving science fiction market in video games, books, and television have all raised the question of future technology that would help people visit these new places of discovery. This situation presents several problems, such as: 1) moving huge distances in a short period of time; 2) by manned spacecraft with people with expected life spans of only 76 to 81 years onboard; 3) using vehicles of some kind that solve questions of food and water storage, medical facilities, quality of life, self-sufficiency, scientific equipment for studying and analyzing data, and a method of communicating the information back home in a real-time fashion — and that is only a few of the problems. Science fiction makes it look simple, but while that is not reality, it does provide inspiration for current imaginative studies on how to explore the universe in new and exciting ways.[16]

However, there is always the question of whether resources should be spent for efforts such as this when the money and scientific effort could go toward solving other problems. While there is much to learn about the vast universe, there are still many unexplored and unanswered questions about life right here on Earth!

The Expanding Universe

> Level 1
> Level 2
> Level 3

MISSION LOG

HUBBLE RELATION
REDSHIFTED
BLUESHIFTED
EXTRA-GALACTIC
    ASTRONOMY
STANDARD CANDLE

In 1929, Edwin Hubble made the remarkable discovery that the universe is expanding. Having established just five years earlier that other galaxies existed, Hubble pioneered the study of other galaxies, a specialty that we now call *extra-galactic astronomy*.

One of his projects was to find the distances to galaxies. This is not easy. It usually requires identifying standard candles within other galaxies. A *standard candle* is an object for which we think that we know the actual brightness, or absolute magnitude. If we measure the apparent magnitude of a standard candle, then we can find the distance. There are several different types of standard candles. We've already mentioned Cepheid variables; they amount to a standard candle. Bright novae, large globular star clusters, and type Ia supernovae are other examples of standard candles.

Earlier we discussed that astronomers can use the Doppler shift to measure how fast a star or other source of light is moving toward or away from us. If an object is moving away from us, its spectrum shifts to longer wavelengths. Since longer wavelength of light corresponds to red light, we say that the light is *redshifted*. Objects moving toward us are *blueshifted*. More than a decade before Hubble's discovery of the expansion of the universe, another astronomer named Vesto Slipher found that most of the "nebulae" that Hubble later showed to be galaxies had large redshifts. In 1929, Hubble showed that the redshifts and distances of galaxies are related. That is, the greater a galaxy's distance, the greater redshift that the galaxy has. If the universe is expanding, then galaxies will be flying apart, and we would expect the sort of relationship between redshift and distance for galaxies that Hubble found. We call this relationship the *Hubble relation*. The most straightforward interpretation of the Hubble relation is that the universe is expanding.

THE STARS OF HEAVEN

I Cor. 15:41

There is one glory of the sun, another glory of the moon, and another glory of the stars; for one star differs from another star in glory.

What does it mean that the universe is expanding? Scientists don't completely know the answer to that question. Imagine that you were an ant on the surface of a balloon and that there were other ants on the balloon as well. If no one was blowing up the balloon or letting air out, and if you don't walk around and if other ants don't walk around, then those ants would appear to be standing still to you. But if someone was blowing up the balloon, you would see the other

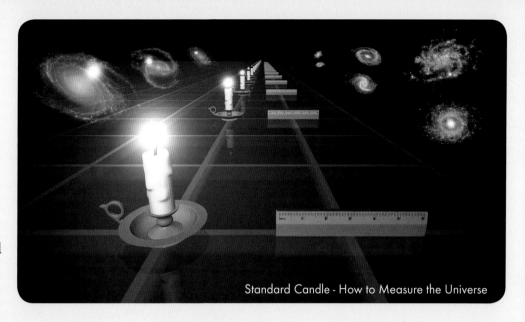

Standard Candle - How to Measure the Universe

ants getting farther away from you, even if none of the ants were moving around. The increasing distance between the ants would be due to the expanding rubber in the balloon. The rate that two ants were to move apart would depend upon the rate of the expansion of the balloon, but also upon how much distance is between the two ants. The greater the distance, the greater the rate the two ants appear to be moving apart. This is exactly what galaxies appear to be doing.

What is the universe expanding into? Nothing, really. The universe is just getting bigger.

Many creationists doubt that the universe is expanding, because they think that it naturally leads to the big-bang theory, something that we shall discuss shortly. However, there are many other conclusions other than the big bang that one can reach about the expanding universe. For instance, in discussing the light-travel-

time problem, we introduced the *white hole theory*. This theory relies upon the universe expanding.

Furthermore, we have already mentioned that the Old Testament tells us that God stretched out the heavens (e.g., Isaiah 40:22). While this may refer to a process during the creation week, it also is possible that this may refer to the expansion of the universe. So, Christians who believe in biblical creation need not fear the expansion of the universe.

Once we establish the Hubble relation, we can turn the process around to find distances to galaxies. We determine the rate of expansion from the Hubble relation. If we measure a galaxy's redshift, then we can use the expansion rate to find the galaxy's distance. This normally is the only method we have for finding the distances of most galaxies, because most galaxies are too far away for us to see standard candles within them.

SPACE
RACE

Exploration of the Galaxy Still a Distant Dream

One of the biggest challenges to any exploration of the universe is the vast distances between objects in space. We simply do not have the technology to move across distant areas of the Milky Way or even between galaxies, including those that are our nearest neighbors. While unmanned probes and vehicles have explored the moon, Mars, and other more distant planets in our solar system, we have been limited in what can be done. NASA has a number of programs working to meet the challenge of creating rockets and other equipment that will allow humans to reach more distant points in space. Many of these include efforts by commercial partners in creating amazing innovations.[17] Vehicles powered with potential warp-drive technology do not currently exist except in science fiction. NASA scientists are studying the potential of this technology as a possible source of power for exploration of our expanding universe. It works by space-time contracting in front of the spacecraft, while expanding behind it.[18]

Something New — Is That for Real?

Often you will see an article about a discovery of a planet, and you will see a beautiful image paired with a sensational headline. The discovery of planet Kepler-10c is a great example! It was reported as the "Godzilla of Earths...a mega-Earth" that weighs 17 times more than Earth and circles a star that scientists compare to our own sun along with a "lava world" called Kepler-10b three times the mass of Earth. It's important to remember that no one knows what the planet actually looks like — it is merely an artist's idea of what it could look like based on available data and assumptions on how it formed based on planets that we are familiar with in our solar system.[19]

Artist's impression of the "Godzilla of Earths" planet.

WONDER WHY?

Most Colorful View of Universe Even among NASA's amazing photo collections, this image of the universe is among the most unique and beautiful! Described as "a comprehensive picture of the evolving universe — among the most colorful deep space images ever captured" by the Hubble Telescope. It is actually a collection of images taken from 2003 to 2012. Said to provide a "missing link" in how stars formed, the studies focus around the growth of galaxies. Yet, many of the theories about the formation and bodies within the universe are unproven and based on a secular timeline of billions of years. There are even very controversial ideas like the multi-universe idea and the string theory, related to additional dimensions.

"The idea of other universes long had been the venue of philosophy and science fiction. When the idea of the multiverse began to be discussed a few decades ago, most astronomers, cosmologists, and physicists considered it pretty silly. However, it began to get traction among cosmologists in the 1990's.... The now widespread belief in the multiverse among cosmologists amounts to a surrender in the war over design. They have painted themselves into a corner, because, even with their big bang cosmogony they are left with strong theistic implications. Unwilling to accept that there may be a God, they in desperation have resorted to defining away the problem. There is no evidence for a multiverse, nor, by definition, could there ever be."[20]

Yet, when you look closer at Earth, the solar system, and even the universe, some remarkably precise things really point to the Creator God of the Bible. Dr. Elizabeth Mitchell has noted, "Our world, and our

universe, seem remarkably fine-tuned. The laws of physics work together so well that Albert Einstein thought the universe had a quality of 'naturalness.' By this he meant that the laws of nature work together because there's just no other way they could. But in fact, they are too fine-tuned, many physicists now think."[21]

Hubble Ultra Deep Field 2014 image with ultraviolet coverage.

CHAPTER 14

Quasars & Active Galaxies

> Level 1
> Level 2
> Level 3

MISSION LOG

RADIO STARS
QUASI-STELLAR
OBJECTS
QUASARS
SYNCHROTRON
RADIATION
SYNCHROTRON SPECTRA

In the 1950s, astronomers developed radio astronomy. Many of the radio sources that they found corresponded with known objects, such as the sun, Jupiter, nebulae, and some galaxies. However, some radio sources appeared to be very faint, blue stars. Stars typically don't produce much emission in the radio part of the spectrum. We detect radio emissions from the sun's corona only because it is so close. Because it was strange for these blue stars to produce so much radio emission, for a while astronomers called these radio-emitting stars "radio stars."

In 1961, astronomers took the first spectrum of one of these radio stars, 3C 273. Its spectrum had only a few emission lines that no one at the time could identify, and the spectrum didn't resemble that of a star at all. Astronomers began calling them *quasi-stellar objects*, abbreviated QSOs. This name quickly was contracted to "quasars."

In 1963, an astronomer determined that the spectrum of 3C 273 had hydrogen emission lines normally visible in the ultraviolet part of the spectrum. To be in the visible part of the spectrum rather than the ultraviolet, 3C 273 had to have a very large redshift. Applying the Hubble law, the distance to 3C 273 was a few billion light years. Knowing the apparent magnitude and distance, astronomers could compute the absolute magnitude. The quasar ended up being about a hundred times brighter than the Milky Way galaxy. This meant that 3C 273 was brighter than a trillion stars.

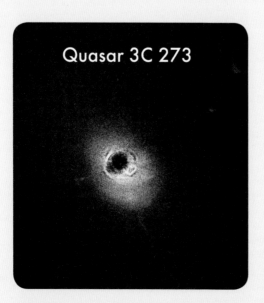

Quasar 3C 273

THE STARS OF HEAVEN

Isaiah 47:13

*You are wearied in
the multitude of your counsels;
Let now the astrologers, the stargazers
And the monthly prognosticators
Stand up and save you
From what shall come upon you.*

The story gets stranger. Astronomers soon found that 3C 273 varied in light with a period of at most a few years. An object can vary in brightness only if some signal can pass through the object to tell the different parts when to brighten and when to fade. The fastest signal that we know is the speed of light, so the size of a varying object is limited by how far light could travel during one cycle of light variation. For instance, if an object takes one year to vary, the object can be no larger than one light year across. The object probably is even smaller. So 3C 273 could be at most a few light years across, but it probably was far smaller. Astronomers quickly found many more quasars. Today there are many thousands of known quasars, with new discoveries nearly every day. The quasar 3C 273 turned out to be the brightest-appearing quasar, and the closest.

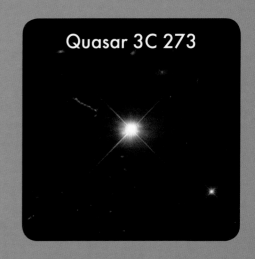

Quasar 3C 273

All quasars have a very large redshift. This suggests that they are very far away. Knowing the distance, we can determine that they are very bright, far brighter than most galaxies. The first quasars found produced much radio emission, but many of the quasars discovered later don't. Their spectra are strange, not resembling stellar spectra at all. The period of light variations suggest that quasars are very small. This presented astronomers with a problem: what is the source of power for something so bright but yet so small? Trillions of stars could power quasars, but that many stars could not fit into such a small size that quasars seem to have. The only theory for powering quasars that seems to work is that they are supermassive black holes. As huge amounts of matter fall into the black hole, the matter is heated to very high temperatures. The high temperature removes electrons from the matter. We say that the matter is ionized, with positively charged atoms and negatively charged free electrons. Very strong magnetic fields interact with the charged particles to produce a special kind of radiation that we call synchrotron radiation. Quasars have synchrotron spectra, which is evidence for this theory.

Soon after quasars were discovered, astronomers found that many quasars were surrounded by faint light "fuzz" that suggested that the fuzz was a galaxy. This led to the idea that quasars are at the centers of galaxies. Over the years, evidence has grown to show that this view likely is true. At the same time, astronomers have found that many galaxies have unusual activity in their cores. Many of these, such as BL Lacertae objects and Seyfert galaxies, are very small and energetic, but not nearly as energetic as quasars. In other words, they resemble quasars, but aren't nearly as powerful, and

usually aren't nearly as far away. Astronomers think that supermassive black holes power the action in the cores of these galaxies.

On the other hand, in recent years astronomers have found evidence of very fast orbital motion in a very small space in the cores of otherwise normal galaxies, including the Milky Way. The superb optics of the HST and other orbiting telescopes has helped tremendously in the discovery of this. We can compute the amount of mass required to drive this orbital motion. It often turns out that the amount of mass required is millions of times the mass of the sun. For instance, the mass at the core of the Milky Way is 2.6 million times the mass of the sun. The nearby galaxy M104 has about a billion times the mass of the sun in its core. There is nothing visible at the cores of these galaxies. The only thing that could fit into the small size there is a black hole.

How do astronomers make sense of this? They think that most large galaxies have supermassive black holes at their cores. Some of these black holes are being fed large amounts of matter. This makes them very bright and energetic. On the other hand, some black holes are starved for matter, making them far less bright. So there is a range from very bright to virtually inactive. The inactive ones would include "normal" galaxies like our own Milky Way.

Artist's impression of a dust-bound supermassive black hole

Among the active galactic nuclei, exactly what we see also depends upon at least two other factors. The matter that falls into the black hole normally doesn't fall directly in, but instead forms a disk around the black hole, and then the matter falls onto the black hole from the disk. At the same time, some matter is ejected along jets perpendicular to the disk. The first factor of what we see is how thick the disk is and how narrow the jets may be. The second factor is the orientation of the disk and jets to our line of sight. If we look directly down one of the jets, what we see will look very different from when we look from the side. Adjusting these parameters, astronomers can explain most quasars and various types of galaxies. Creationists easily can agree with much of this theory.

Nearby Galaxy
NGC_6744

What causes the varying rates at which the supermassive galaxies are fed? Most astronomers think that the rate has to do with age. According to this theory, young galaxies feed large amounts of matter to the young quasars that they contain. With time, the amount of available matter that can fall into the black holes decreases. However, this relies upon billions of years of time. Since the Bible indicates that the world is only thousands of years old, many creationists reject this thinking.

CHAPTER 15

Cosmology

> Level 1
> Level 2
> Level 3

MISSION LOG

COSMOLOGY
FILAMENTS
VOIDS
STEADY-STATE THEORY
CONTINUOUS-CREATION
   THEORY
BIG-BANG THEORY
COSMIC MICROWAVE
   BACKGROUND
HORIZON PROBLEM
FLATNESS PROBLEM

Cosmology is the study of the structure of the universe. For instance, the geocentric and heliocentric theories are cosmologies. Today, we generally think of cosmology as referring to the largest scales of the universe, the distribution of galaxies. Cosmologists are physicists or astronomers who specialize in the study of cosmology. We've already seen that galaxies normally group together into clusters. These clusters tend to be along lines and sheets and loop around, leaving large, mostly open spaces inside. Astronomers call these open spaces *voids*. This gives the galaxy distribution a sort of lace appearance. Astronomers call the lines and sheets of galaxy clusters *filaments*. Together, the filaments and voids resemble very holey Swiss cheese.

The ancient Greeks thought that the universe was eternal, without beginning and without end. This, too, is a cosmology. The ancient Greek gods were very limited in power, not much more than supermen. Thus, their gods clearly lacked the power to create the world. Nor could the ancient Greeks conceive of a natural origin for the universe. So it was easier for them to think that the universe had always existed. In the late Roman period, Christianity rapidly replaced the ancient Greek and Roman religions and their many gods. Unfortunately, many supposed Christians weren't true believers, and many people retained ancient pagan ideas. Belief in an eternal universe was one of those ideas. Even true believers had difficulty breaking away from this, and so belief in an eternal universe persisted until well into the 20th century. However, Genesis 1:1 clearly states that there was a beginning to the universe. If people had taken the first verse of the Bible seriously, they would have rejected belief in an eternal universe.

THE STARS OF HEAVEN

Genesis 1:1

In the beginning God created the heavens and the earth.

When Edwin Hubble showed that the universe is expanding, astronomers naturally wondered what this meant in terms of cosmology. Since most astronomers thought that the universe was eternal, they thought that the universe always had expanded and always would expand. However, if the universe had been expanding forever, its mass ought to have been spread out very thinly a long time ago. If this were the case, then we ought not to see other clusters of galaxies, but we do. How can this be? Many astronomers believed that as the universe expanded, new matter simply popped into existence to maintain a constant density in the universe. Cosmologists called this the *steady-state theory*, because the universe remained unchanging. An alternate name was the *continuous-creation theory*, because it required the continual creation of new matter to maintain constant density. If the universe is eternal, with neither beginning nor end, then there is no place for a creator, so this amounts to an atheistic cosmology.

While the steady-state theory was popular, because it fit well with the belief in an eternal universe, other astronomers began to think that perhaps the expansion of the universe suggested that the universe had a beginning. If the universe is expanding, then one might expect that in the past the universe was much smaller. The density and temperature would have been much higher in the past, too. If we were to trace this billions of years back into the past, the universe would have been far too hot and dense for stars and other structures as we now know them to exist. This sort of thinking leads to the big-bang theory. The big-bang theory says that the universe began about 13.8 billion years ago in a very hot, dense state and has been expanding and cooling since, so that we now have the universe that we see.

Both the steady-state and big-bang theories were developed by 1948, and debate over which theory, if either, was true lasted about two decades. During this time, most astronomers preferred the steady-state theory. In 1965, two astronomers announced the discovery of the *cosmic microwave background* (CMB). The CMB is radiation of a particular type in the microwave part of the spectrum that is coming from all directions. According to the big-bang theory, the CMB comes from a time a few hundred thousand

The Holmdel Horn Antenna on which Penzias and Wilson discovered the cosmic microwave background.

years after the big bang when the universe was still very hot and dense. If the big-bang theory is true, the universe must have the CMB. On the other hand, the CMB cannot exist in a steady-state universe. Thus, the discovery of the CMB appears to disprove the steady-state theory. Since the only remaining theory at the time was the big bang, the big bang has become the dominant cosmology.

Many Christians think that the big bang was God's method of creation. Some think that the first verse of the Bible, "In the beginning God created the heavens and the earth," speaks of the big bang. Others think that the creation of light in verse 3 was the big bang. However, there are problems with this. One problem is that the earth is mentioned in the very first verse, but according to the big-bang theory, the earth did not exist until the solar system formed more than nine billion years after the big bang. Another problem is that according to the big-bang theory, many stars existed billions of years before the earth, but we know from Genesis 1 that God made stars after the earth. Another problem is that the Bible suggested that the creation was only thousands of years ago, not billions of years ago.

There are scientific problems with the big-bang theory. For instance, the CMB has a light-travel-time problem. Different parts of the CMB have precisely the same temperature, though light from each part has not had enough time to reach light in each part. Cosmologists call this the *horizon problem*. Cosmologists suggest that in the early universe (a tiny fraction of a second after the big bang), the universe experienced inflation. Inflation is a hypothetical rapid expansion, an expansion far faster than the speed of light. Virtually in an instant, the universe may have gone from something the size of an atom to millions of light years across. Inflation supposedly solves the horizon problem and another problem called the *flatness problem*. Most astronomers and cosmologists think that inflation really happened. Some astronomers think that there is evidence for inflation, but this is debatable.

The clumping structure of galaxies. In order for this structure to exist, there must have been slight differences in density in the early universe. These slight variations in density ought to show up as slight differences in temperature in the CMB. Cosmologists call these temperature differences *temperature fluctuations*. In 1989, NASA launched the COBE (Cosmic Background Explorer) satellite to measure the temperature fluctuations predicted by the theory. After a two-year mission, the COBE failed to find the predicted temperature fluctuations. It was only after some very subtle studies that scientists were able to see hints of temperature fluctuations ten times less than predicted. Other experiments and space missions since then have confirmed these temperature fluctuations. Now cosmologists claim that the measurements and predictions agree. How can they say that? After they discovered the actual temperature fluctuations, they altered the big-bang model to fit the data.

There have been many other changes in the big-bang theory over the years. It is instructive to compare the big-bang model of the early 1980s to today's big-bang model. The expansion rate of the earlier model was less than today's model. Consequently, the age of the universe back then was assumed to be 16 to 18 billion years. Today, the age is supposed to be 13.8 billion years, give or take 1 percent. In the earlier model, no one considered inflation, but today all big-bang models contain inflation. The same is true of dark matter. In 1998, astronomers began to think that there is some sort of force in the universe that causes space to repel itself, thus accelerating expansion. Astronomers call this dark energy. Obviously the earlier big-bang model did not include dark energy, but big-bang models today do. Theoretical physicists think that they can best describe matter if there are at least six extra dimensions of space. They call this *string theory*. In the earlier big-bang model, string theory was not included, but it normally is today.

Obviously, the big-bang model has changed tremendously in recent years, and we can expect that the model will continue to change. Scientists had complete confidence in the earlier model, just as they have total confidence in today's big-bang model. Yet, those two models bear almost no resemblance to one another. So, which model is true — the old, or the new one, or one that no one has yet thought of? This illustrates how quickly man's ideas can change, but we can be assured that God and His Word do not change. The history of science shows that virtually every idea man comes up with eventually is discarded. If we interpret the Bible in terms of the big bang, it will do tremendous damage to the integrity of Scripture when the big bang is discarded.

It probably will be some time before scientists abandon the big-bang model. In order to abandon the model, there must be a replacement, but there is no evolutionary possibility out there. As new problems and challenges arise, cosmologists will alter the big bang to solve them. Many people view this as a strength of the model. However, it could be its eventual undoing. Recall that the Ptolemaic model lasted for 1,500 years. Its strength was that whenever there was a disagreement between the model predictions and observation, one could easily fix the problem by adding new epicycles. While this solved each problem, it made the Ptolemaic model increasingly complex. It was its complexity that eventually caused scientists to abandon the Ptolemaic model in favor of the simpler heliocentric model. It's not that the Ptolemaic model was disproved. Indeed, if one can freely alter a model to meet each new challenge, then the model can never be disproved. But if a model cannot be disproved, is it really scientific?

Conclusion

I hope that you have enjoyed reading this book and that you've learned much about astronomy from it. Perhaps one day you will become an astronomer to help other people understand more about God's creation. There are many other fine resources, such as books and videos, about astronomy that can teach you more. Often you can find these in your school or public library. However, you must always check what they tell you with what God's Word, the Bible says. There are many online resources, such as those at the Answers in Genesis website (https://answersingenesis.org/). Many of these can teach you far more about creation.

If you visit the Answers in Genesis Creation Museum, you can enjoy a planetarium show at the Stargazers Planetarium there. The shows at the Stargazers Planetarium entertain, educate, but, more importantly, give God the glory for His wonderful creation.

THE STARS OF HEAVEN

Psalm 147:4

He counts the number of the stars;

He calls them all by name.

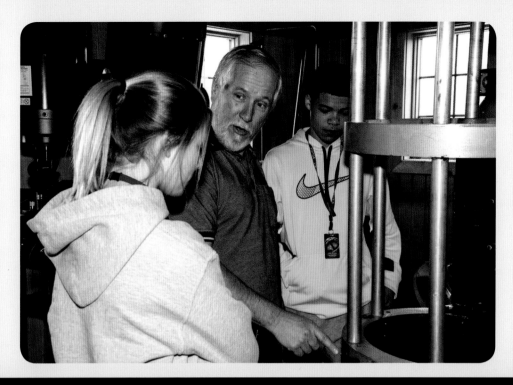

Astronomer and author Dr. Danny Faulkner of the Answers in Genesis ministry explains components of a large telescope in the Johnson Observatory near Cincinnati, Ohio. The observatory is the site of a number of special presentations and viewings of the night sky. (Upper left) A planetarium show in the Stargazers Planetarium at the Creation Museum. (Lower left) The April 2012 dedication of Johnson Observatory at the Creation Museum.

Project Moon-Blink

The Johnson Observatory at the Creation Museum near Cincinnati contains a variety of telescopes, but one is very special. The Johnsonian telescope, named for its Christian inventor, Lyle T. Johnson, was used in Project Moon-Blink, a special program of NASA in the mid-1960s before manned lunar landings to study anomalies (gases, etc) on the moon. Johnson's invention was so innovative, a new class of telescopes — Johnsonian — is named after him. The Johnson family approved the decision to donate the telescope to the Creation Museum because of Johnson's faith and belief that God was the creator of the universe.[22]

The Creation Museum also is home of Johnson Observatory. The observatory has several telescopes, including two 16-inch reflectors. Weather permitting, Johnson Observatory offers opportunities to view the moon, planets, nebulae, star clusters, and galaxies. And there is a daytime program for looking at sunspots and prominences on the sun.

Winter

Even without a telescope you can see many constellations on clear nights. The season of the year in which you are looking at the night sky will determine which constellations and other objects like stars or individual planet you may be able to see the best. Constellations visible in the winter and spring include Orion, Taurus, Gemini, Canis Major, Ursa Major, and Leo.

Spring

Summer

Summer can be a wonderful time to view the night sky! If you are watching the movements of the stars and planets, be sure to include a notebook to make notes on what you see. Keep an eye out for Bootes, Lyra, Cygnus, Scorpius, and Sagittarius. The summer Milky Way viewed through binoculars can be stunning!

Late Summer

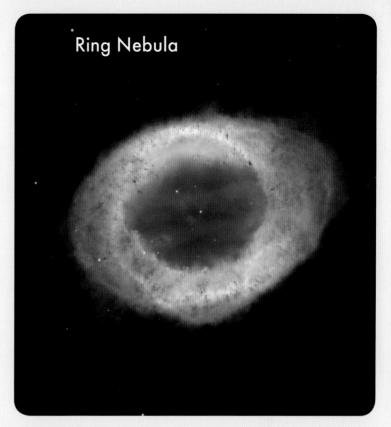

Ring Nebula

Endnotes

[1] *The American Heritage® Dictionary of the English Language,* Fourth Edition copyright, 2000, Houghton Mifflin Company. Updated in 2009. Houghton Mifflin Company.

[2] http://www.dailymail.co.uk/sciencetech/article-2617054/Race-ed-planet-Russia-says-YES-building-super-rocket-rival-Nasas-designs-hopes-getting-Mars-2030.htm

[3] http://www.nasa.gov/content/nasa-s-search-for-asteroids-to-help-protect-earth/#.U2QIw_ldV8E

[4] http://curator.jsc.nasa.gov/lunar/laboratory_tour.cfm

[5] http://www.iau.org/news/pressreleases/detail/iau1303/

[6] http://www.iau.org/

[7] http://www.jwst.nasa.gov/

[8] http://jwst.nasa.gov/about.html

[9] "A Final Visit," http://hubblesite.org/the_telescope/hubble_essentials/

[10] http://en.wikipedia.org/wiki/We_choose_to_go_to_the_Moon

[11] "Just Right for Life" by Danny Faulkner, December 2013, https://answersingenesis.org/astronomy/extrasolar-planets/just-right-for-life

[12] http://hubblesite.org/newscenter/archive/releases/2012/07/full/; http://en.wikipedia.org/wiki/Milky_Way

[13] http://en.wikipedia.org/wiki/Milky_Way

[14] http://listverse.com/2013/11/24/10-mind-bending-facts-about-the-milky-way-galaxy/

[15] http://www.universetoday.com/22285/facts-about-the-milky-way/

[16] http://www.nasa.gov/externalflash/human_space/

[17] http://www.nasa.gov/exploration/home/index.html

[18] http://www.nbcnews.com/science/space/how-quantum-thruster-physics-could-make-warp-drive-reality-f8C11015234

[19] http://www.foxnews.com/science/2014/06/02/godzilla-earths-alien-planet-17-times-heavier-than-our-world-discovered/

[20] "Just Right for Life" by Danny Faulkner, December 2013, https://answersingenesis.org/astronomy/extrasolar-planets/just-right-for-life/

[21] "Are We One of Many, or Did God Design the Universe with Physics That Actually Works?" by Dr. Elizabeth Mitchell, August 3, 2013, https://answersingenesis.org/physics/higgs-boson-god-particle/are-we-one-of-many-or-did-god-design-the-universe-with-physics-that-actually-works/

[22] http://ntrs.nasa.gov/archive/nasa/casi.ntrs.nasa.gov/19660030253.pdf

Our Award-Winning
Wonders of Creation Series

Filled with special features, every exciting title includes over 200 beautiful full-color photos and illustrations, practical hands-on learning experiments, charts, graphs, glossary, and index — it's no wonder these books have become one of our most requested series.

- **The Mineral Book*** reveals the first mention of minerals in the Bible and their value in culture and society.
- **The Ecology Book*** researches the relationship between living organisms and our place in God's wondrous creation.
- **The Archaeology Book*** uncovers ancient history from alphabets to ziggurats.
- **The Cave Book** digs deep into the hidden wonders beneath the surface.
- **The New Astronomy Book*** soars through the solar system separating myth from fact.
- **The Geology Book** provides a tour of the earth's crust pointing out the beauty and the scientific evidences for creation.
- **The Fossil Book** explains everything about fossils while also demonstrating the shortcomings of the evolutionary theory.
- **The New Ocean Book*** explores the depths of the ocean to find the mysteries of the deep.
- **The New Weather Book*** delves into all weather phenomena, including modern questions of supposed climate change.

*This title is color-coded with three educational levels in mind: 5th to 6th grades, 7th to 8th grades, and 9th through 11th grades.

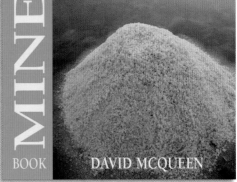

8 1/2 x 11 • Casebound • 96 pages • Full-color interior
ISBN-13: 978-0-89051-802-1

JR. HIGH to HIGH SCHOOL

sample interior from The Archaeology Book

The Ecology Book
ISBN-13: 978-0-89051-701-7

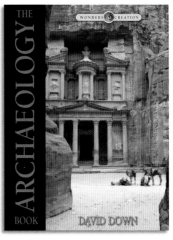

The Archaeology Book
ISBN-13: 978-0-89051-573-0

The New Ocean Book
ISBN-13: 978-0-89051-905-9

The Geology Book
ISBN-13: 978-0-89051-281-4

The New Weather Book
ISBN-13: 978-0-89051-861-8

The New Astronomy Book
ISBN-13: 978-0-89051-834-2

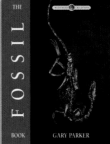

The Fossil Book
ISBN-13: 978-0-89051-438-2

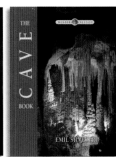

The Cave Book
ISBN-13: 978-0-89051-496-2

EXPLORATION OF OUR SOLA

Then God made two great lights: the greater light to rule th
and the lesser light to rule the night. *He made* the stars c
Genesis 1:16

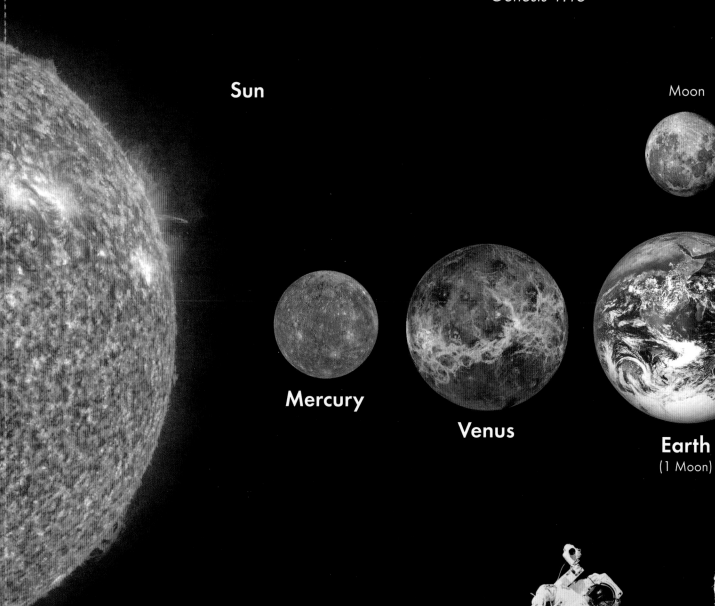

Sun

Moon

Mercury

Venus

Earth
(1 Moon)

Bruce McCandless II from Space Shuttle
Challenger First use of the Manned
Maneuvering Unit (MMU)

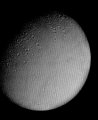

Prometheus

Pandora

Titan

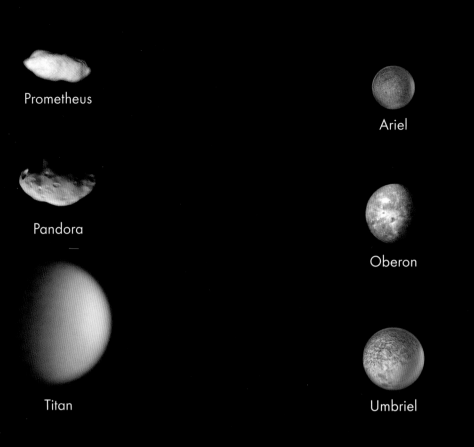

Saturn
(62 Known Moons
and Hundreds of
Moonlets)

Enceladus

Ariel

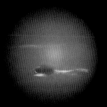

Oberon

Umbriel

Uranus
(27+ Moons)

Titania

Miranda

Triton

Neptune
(14+ Moons)

Nereid

R SYSTEM

e day,
lso.

Io

Callisto

Phobos

Mars
(2 Moons)

Jupiter
(67+ Moons)

Deimos

Ganymede

Space Shuttle
Challenger

Europa